THE SCEPTICAL WITNESS

Stuart Kind

THE SCEPTICAL WITNESS

Concerning the Scientific Investigation of Crime against a Human Background

FOREWORD BY

P D James

Distributed by

THE FORENSIC SCIENCE SOCIETY

First Published (1999) by

HODOLOGY Ltd.
books@highwayman.demon.co.uk

Distributed by
The Forensic Science Society
18a Mount Parade, Harrogate
Yorkshire, England, HG1 1BX
tel. 01423 506068
books@fscisoc.demon.co.uk
www.demon.co.uk/forensic

ISBN 0 9533987 0 6

Life can only be understood backwards; but it must be lived forwards

Sören Kierkegaard

FOR

EVELYN

ACKNOWLEDGEMENTS

I wish to thank all my family, friends and colleagues who, wittingly or unwittingly, helped me to write this book.

And to thank (no harm in thanking) all those rogues without whom I should not have had a job.

FOREWORD

by

P D James

When I was a girl I don't think I ever heard the words forensic science, nor I imagine did most policemen. Today we all know what a vital part science plays in the in the detection of crime and no police force could successfully operate without the help of its regional forensic science laboratory. There have, of course been many books about the achievements of science, but only too often books by experts fail to satisfy because those with knowledge aren't good at communicating it, and those who write well have less knowledge. This certainly isn't true of Stuart Kind, one of this country's most distinguished forensic biologists. *The Sceptical Witness* is more than a fascinating account of the achievements, the limitations and the complications of science in the service of the law. Here we have an enthralling and excellently written account of a life and a philosophy as well as of a career, told with honesty and candour.

Throughout the voice is strongly personal so that we feel we are listening to Professor Kind as he moves in memory from a childhood in a small terraced house in the Meadows district of Nottingham, to his various early jobs, lab assistant and lorry driver among them, to service in the RAF as an air navigator, and finally to a career in forensic science which led him to the summit of his profession. It was the war which gave him his chance. During it he dropped at first bombs on Germany and then food for the starving civilians of Holland and, when the war ended, he took advantage of the special provisions for ex-servicemen, used his free time to study and finally became a student at Nottingham University.

But the book is more than a chronological account of a career. Stuart Kind is not dominated by time. His memory moves backwards and forwards over a wide plateau of experience from childhood to retirement, and in doing so he describes the development of the forensic science service during the last fifty years. He has, of course, fascinating tales to tell, including the part he played in the case of the Yorkshire Ripper, the killer who terrorised the North of England in 1980. Stuart Kind was one of a small group which included senior police officers of the Metropolitan Police who were called in to advise. He describes the methods he used to attempt to pinpoint the area where the Ripper was likely to strike again. In the event he was fortuitously caught, but Professor Kind's analytical reasoning was proved accurate.

The chapter headings give clues to the contents: Early Investigations; Murder, Rape and Arson; Fear and Fraud; Red Herrings and Jigsaws. Forensic Scientists, like police officers, see the worst that human beings are capable of doing to each other, but *The Sceptical Witness* is no mere recital of horrors. This is an account of a life and a distinguished career which will appeal to the general reader as much as it does to the scientist.

CONTENTS

Preface

If an author claims impartiality for his views he seldom lies. He probably believes that he is impartial. Dealing with such authors can be more dangerous than dealing with liars. Lies can be exposed but the exposure of bias in the judgements of the good is much more difficult. Yet the belief in one's own impartiality is widespread amongst authors. In my library I have three books where each title begins with "The Truth About...". They make an interesting study for the sceptical reader.

I gave up any conviction of objective neutrality in my own judgements long ago, although that belief lasted rather longer than did my faith in scientific high-mindedness. This latter concept was an early casualty in my scientific career, as readers of this book will see. But this is not a confession of malice. It is a statement of my belief that none of us can be totally impartial, much as we would like to be or strive to be. We can only interpret our personal experiences according to our own nature and nurture and do the best that we can to make a balanced judgement. The very least we must do is to try very hard to be objective where the circumstances require it.

As individuals we receive a set of personal defining factors at the moment of our conception and these factors, the genes, provide the canvas upon which the individual life picture is subsequently painted. The picture cannot stretch beyond the confines of the canvas but, within its bounds, an infinity of images is possible. Between birth and death just one of these images becomes the unique definition of the individual, no matter how "ordinary" he or she may be. Human society is made up of a very large number of these unique individuals. During the evolution of human society, patterns of discovery develop in the three main areas of human culture: art, science and religion. Themes are abstracted from experience, and these become the schools in art, the theories in science and the dogmas in religion. But all these are the products of the human mind with all its imperfections and its constant striving to see pattern and permanence in the conflict of human experience.

The Sceptical Witness

Both scientific research and crime investigation are examples of this search for pattern and, although we may finally congratulate ourselves that we have discovered material certainties, we must always keep in mind that these certainties are distilled from what we take to be "physical reality", through a complex of human imperfections, into the singular intellect. Because of this, any account of the experiences of one individual in forensic science must contain a large component of autobiography. The narrative is influenced throughout by the character of the narrator. So the reader should not only know what story he is getting but, as far as possible, the prejudices of the author. This is a tall order for any writer. He must show, as far as he can, not only the whole picture but also the canvas upon which it is painted. So I propose to start this story right at the beginning, or at least as near to the beginning as I can remember.

I claim nothing in the book as original except for the descriptive narrative. If you think you recognise something in the text as your own idea, you are probably right. But "when you steal from one author, it's plagiarism; if you steal from many , it's research". Put another way I am in the same position as the burglar who admits to possessing so many stolen goods that he can't remember where the individual pieces come from.

Writing the book was a fascinating experience for me. I felt as if I were a historian quarrying old records, searching for causal chains in human affairs. Or perhaps it was more like being a crime investigator, newly posted to a long running, unsuccessful murder investigation, who examines a mass of old reports and statements and tries to see evidence where, until then, everyone else has seen only information. There was even one instance when, on mulling over the facts of a forty year old case, I suddenly realised that they were only explicable by the case being a "set up". There is no cause for general alarm at this revelation, or for cries of "injustice" or "corruption", because no criminal charge resulted. Nevertheless I inserted an account of the case later in the book because it displays some attitudes towards forensic science in those early days. Happily such attitudes have long since changed.

Preface

Although the story as I tell it is roughly chronological I have refused to be ruled by sequence. Time, as a humorist once said, is a device to prevent everything happening at once but the human mind is unrestricted by time and we can reminisce backward and imagine forward at will. "The further back one looks the further forward one can see" (often attributed to Churchill) is the essence of discovery.

The story often takes the form of incidents and cases taken out of time sequence and placed in the subject context in order to illustrate themes. Many of these can be read independently of the others so, if you prefer to dip rather than to read systematically, you can do so. But whichever you do, the narrative is essentially a single picture. Everything is connected to everything else, as the philosopher said.

In those passages where I describe but omit to name, please don't ask. Like the murder investigator you must work it all out for yourself. So here it is. It is imbued with the spirit contained in the aphorism of the forensic pathologist Keith Simpson:

One should swear to tell the truth (as one sees it), the whole truth (as far as one knows it), and nothing but the truth (so as not to commit perjury). No-one can do more.

Stuart Stanley Kind
Harrogate, April 1999

Chapter One: First Evidence

I was born on the twenty first day of January 1925, at 103 Kingsmeadow Road, a small terrace house in the Meadows district of Nottingham. This statement I make with confidence because, although I do not recollect the event myself, there is adequate documentary and testimonial evidence to support my belief. We develop most of our beliefs, and we make most of the important decisions in our lives, by relying upon the statements of others. From similar evidence I know that I bear the name Kind because that is my father's name, the name Stanley because that is my mother's maiden name and the name Stuart because that is the name of the kindly Scottish midwife who assisted my entry into the 1920s world of the English working classes.

I was the youngest of a family of three boys, the eldest of whom was ten years older than I. My between brother was a mere sixteen months older than I and, because he was physically slight for his age, for some years people took us for twins. However we were very different in character. Whereas he was extrovert, daredevil and impulsive I was introvert and cautious to the point of cowardliness. The development of my character away from these undesirable characteristics was gravely inhibited by my brother who took it upon himself to resolve my disputes with other children. This he did by imposing his own rough and summary judicial procedure upon anyone who appeared to be a threat to me. First sentence, then verdict, then trial, then evidence, then charge. The last four stages were facultative. Such can be the effect of an age difference of a mere sixteen months when one is young.

My earliest memory is of riding a three-wheeled bicycle on the pavement outside my house when I was three years old, together with a friend who was two years older. Coincidentally I have just spoken on the telephone with this same friend before sitting down at the keyboard. He is now 73 and I am 71. My eldest brother is happily still with us at the age of 81 and is still possessed of many of those human faculties which allow the living of an enjoyable life. My second brother, my guardian through so many childish disputes, would have been 72 at this time had fate not dictated that, at the age of 19 years, he was forced to bale out from a stricken Halifax bomber over the south coast of England. A northerly wind caused his parachute to drift out to sea and, within the sight of home on a summer's day in 1943, this young man's life ended in the English Channel. His body was never found. Thereafter his mother left the front door of the house permanently unlocked until the day she died, just in case he came home. I seldom consider humanity's concept of justice without thinking about him.

I grew up under poor conditions but I can't remember feeling particularly disadvantaged. Children are amazingly resilient and adaptable, and we were no worse off than most other working class families who lived nearby. The nineteen thirties were a period of high unemployment in England and my father was out of a job for much of the time but, from a child's point of view, we were a normal family living an ordinary life. Even now I cannot conceive of a fulfilled human life except in a family framework. We were poor but everyone else we knew was, on the same scale of measurement, "poor". Our family circumstances were ameliorated by the fact that, during the hardest times, my eldest brother donned the mantle of breadwinner.

Financial problems were occasionally exacerbated by my father, an irrepressible optimist, deciding that he could better our lot by predicting which horse would be first past the post. Possibly this characteristic is genetically inherited because, later in life, I developed the view that the best test of a scientific hypothesis is a similarly predictive one. If you can win money by betting on it then it is a good hypothesis. This was a view which, when I was a working forensic scientist, I kept to myself. I did not wish to give my superior officers in the world of government forensic science any further cause for regret that they had promoted me to positions of authority. Pure flippancy you say? Well if sometime you have nothing better to do, lean back and think it through.

My father was a kindly man with a good level of scholarship such as seemed to be more common amongst working class people in those days than in these. He seldom drank alcohol, perhaps a glass of port at Christmas, but in common with most men of his social class he smoked heavily. He had a resolute and penetrating sense of humour which he

Chapter One: First Evidence

maintained until he died, a few days short of his ninetieth birthday. Lonely after my mother's comparatively early death he remarried some years after I began my post-war career as a forensic scientist. Thereafter he spent the last quarter century of his life living with, and being harried by, the Devil's protégé on earth. This lady survived him and lived on until her middle nineties when she went to rejoin her maker. I remember feeling rather sorry for Old Nick. I can't help but think that he must have met his match in her. Poor devil.

I only once in my life seriously considered murder and this lady was to be the intended victim. Because of my father's unhappiness I tried reasoning with her, threatening her and regularly bribing her with sums of money to try to get her to show some tolerance towards my father's undisputed faults but all this produced no result. Desperate to alleviate my father's wretchedness I tried every legitimate method I could think of but no improvement in behaviour lasted more than a few hours. So I began to consider a more lasting solution. Several methods of dispatch were considered and I think any one of them would have worked without suspicion being aroused. After all, by that time murder was a regular constituent of my life as a forensic scientist.

In the event I never tried. I don't think it was lack of nerve. Perhaps it was a natural revulsion at killing someone on a one-to-one basis. It was quite different from the anonymous mass killing of my days as a wartime bomber crew member. On the other hand perhaps I inherited some of my father's optimism and retained a residual belief that things would someday, somehow, improve. My father's optimism always surfaced at the times when he was most tormented by life. On one occasion I visited him in hospital when he was in his eighties and seriously ill. I was with him when he recovered consciousness, in the geriatric ward, and I remember him looking wryly about him at the heaps of ancient human wreckage in the other beds. He looked at me, smiled, and said "It looks like the forward line of Nottingham Forest". His favourite football team was going through a bad patch.

The Sceptical Witness

I frequently digress from a narrative but I hope I digress well. Controlled digression is a good antidote to the tedious daily necessity to consider most things in place and sequence. It is one of the factors which allow us to bond together the patchwork of experience which makes up our mental and physical life. It is also a most enjoyable relaxation, particularly for a forensic scientist whose life is ruled by dates and times, both at the investigation and trial stages of his work. The most accomplished practitioner of controlled digression I've ever known was also a forensic scientist. He was much senior to me and he had a long standing international reputation in his field of expertise. Many found him to be an intimidating personality. Once I went to a lecture given by him when he was long into retirement. He appeared a huge figure in the small theatre where he was lecturing. Standing right at the front of the stage, towering over the footlights, he was dressed in a shabby sports jacket over a shabbier cardigan which hung almost down to his knees. He was so close to the edge of the platform that a single pace forward would have put him over the footlights and into the audience. Each time he appeared about to step forward there was a sharp intake of breath from the audience. But he never fell, although I think he left the audience a little drained by the sustained tension. I had a notion that perhaps he was doing it deliberately, for his own malicious enjoyment.

He spoke in a precise and lilting Welsh voice and I remember I closed my eyes and imagined him as the king in Shakespeare's *Henry the Fifth*. Part way through his long talk he digressed, and his digression gradually took him away from the thread of his highly technical discourse. I returned from my own mental ramblings in the world of the Elizabethan theatre and I began to feel sorry for him. He was old and I doubted if he could ever find his way back from his diversion to his main theme. It is never a pleasant experience to witness the deteriorating faculties of an accomplished scholar. Reluctantly I decided that all was lost and that this man, of world-wide stature, was about to depart the international scientific stage in a sad mixture of confused ideas and rambling presentation.

Chapter One: First Evidence

My prediction seemed finally to be confirmed when he digressed from his digression. He appeared to be caught up in an expository shambles, a scientific fly caught up in a logical spider's web where his meanderings only served to entrap him even more. The mixed sympathy and scorn of his young scientific audience seemed to be the inevitable fate that faced him. Disaster seemed assured. Even the sharpest mind in the world, belonging to someone in the prime of youth, would have had the greatest difficulty extracting itself from the myriad of interwoven and interlocked threads of narrative, argument and lyrical prosody that his lecture had now become. Away he went into some sort of Celtic dreamland where individual themes and ideas began to lose their lucid outline and to mingle in a kaleidoscopic thought world which had, or perhaps hadn't, a tenuous connection with the subject of his lecture.

Sitting in the audience I think my jaw was hanging open as I listened to a performance which would have drawn accolades from theatre critics if not from scientists. I rather liked the old villain and I didn't savour the prospect of him being derided by lesser men and women so I mentally began to compose questions which might do something to rescue his reputation during the post-lecture discussion period. Perhaps I could do this by implying profound and erudite connections between some of his more abstruse utterances and the real world of forensic science. I wanted to erase the contempt which was beginning to show on the faces of some of the audience. That was the only way I could recover the situation, to imply connections where none existed. Nothing discomfits a scientist more effectively than the idea that he has missed the point and that everyone else has seen it. Scientists do so like to be omniscient.

But I needn't have worried. Our veteran scientist did it all for himself and he did it faultlessly. Without any semblance of strain or awkwardness he seamlessly and effortlessly returned from his secondary digression to his primary digression and then, just as seamlessly and effortlessly, he returned from that to his main discourse. It was a masterly performance. I was left with a feeling of relief mixed with admiration and envy. He had been totally in control the whole time. His lecture now seemed an organic whole, a beautifully designed presentation by a master of communication with not a single word superfluous or out of place. The old devil had been playing with his adolescent audience all along. What a performance. What a captain. He would have been marvellous as Henry the Fifth.

Rather less seamlessly I now return to the small terrace house in the Nottingham Meadows where we lived under conditions which would provoke the deep concern of professional carers if judged by today's material standards. But it is simply a case of "other days other ways". Perhaps I might have been equally appalled by the circumstances under which my mother had lived as a child in the late nineteenth century. Somehow I doubt it though. The pace of change in human society quickens with the passage of time and I have no doubt that my childhood in the twenties and thirties had much more in common with conditions in the nineteenth century than it has with life in the late twentieth century.

Heating for the family house was by a single small open fire in a black metal range in the kitchen. The range was kept a meticulously polished black by the daily application of "black lead", a substance which was applied with a soft brush and which had the capacity to make both fire grates and the hands of small boys brilliantly black beyond the limits of imagination. The kitchen was also the living room, the dining room and, with the addition of a zinc galvanised bath placed just in front of the fire, it became the bathroom. Water for the bath was heated in a boiler on the right hand side of the range and when it was required it was ladled out with the help of an old saucepan. The fire was well stoked for such occasions to ensure ample hot water and this also had the effect of warming the kitchen although, to bare childish skin, the effect was sometimes uncomfortably one sided.

I remember, on one occasion, noticing with fascination a dead cockroach in the saucepan of hot water as it was being transferred to the bath. It was pure white, the result of lengthy aqueous extraction at

Chapter One: First Evidence

boiling point, and it swirled aimlessly around the pan until my mother removed it with a stick of firewood and threw it into the fire. Neither of us mentioned it. It would not do for it to be widely known that a cockroach had been seen in the house. Stimulated by such knowledge, local gossip would soon have turned it into a horde of the little black beasts rather than a single pallid and very dead minor arthropod. There were "clean houses" and "dirty houses" you understand and a correct hygienic classification was a priceless thing in the society in which we lived. I felt no revulsion as I stepped into the bath. The knowledge that I shared the bathwater with the cockroach gave me no qualms at all, and the cockroach itself was no longer in a position to consider the desirability of sharing it with me.

To the left side of the fire grate was the oven which, in common with the boiler, was heated through its side wall. However there was a difference because the oven side wall could become cherry red if the fire was hot. This was sometimes a cause of the skin on our rice puddings being rather variable, ranging from a very dark brown on the hot side of the oven through a gentle golden colour in the centre to a pale cream on the cool side. It didn't really matter, it was all eaten. My omnivorous nature today must owe something to these influences. Omnivorous did I say? Well my wife will doubtless read this script and she will assuredly point out to me that I do not like rice pudding skin. Shall we then say "omnivorous except for rice pudding skin"? As a scientific editor of many years' experience I always exhorted my authors towards precision and I suppose I must now practise what I have always preached.

Lighting in our small terrace house was by coal gas, a malodorous and highly poisonous product which was manufactured by roasting coal in furnaces at the local gas works and then piping the product to the consumer. Because the gas was so smelly there was little chance that a conscious and able bodied person would be accidentally poisoned by it. But it was a most efficacious way of departing from this world for those who had a mind to do so. Coal gas contains a high content of carbon monoxide and it is this substance which ensures a successful outcome for those with suicidal intent. This is because carbon monoxide has the strange property of combining with the blood very much better than oxygen. Because blood is the carrier of the oxygen which is necessary for life, any interference with its oxygen carrying capacity tends to be fatal. The molecular nests which are reserved in blood, by Nature, for the oxygen molecule nestlings, are taken up by carbon monoxide cuckoos. The benign oxygen is thus excluded from its natural home and painless suffocation results. Thus, putting ones head into the gas oven was the preferred (if that is the correct word) method of suicide of those days.

Town gas, as it was called, remained in use until after I became a forensic scientist in the early fifties and we regularly dealt with analyses of blood samples, in suspected coal gas poisonings, in the laboratories of the time. Nowadays such laboratory analyses are more usually associated with the accidental carbon monoxide poisonings generated by the combination of poor ventilation and a naked flame of burning natural gas. Natural gas, unlike the old fashioned town gas, is not in itself poisonous but with limited burning it generates carbon monoxide just like the old coking ovens of the town gasworks did.

When darkness fell in our small house we used to ignite the gas light with a spill of lighted paper newspaper. Taking the lighted spill in one hand we opened the valve with the other by pulling down on a chain which actuated the gaspipe valve. A similar chain on the other side of the light fitting served to close it. There was something of an art in igniting the gaslight because, if the mantle was touched, it disintegrated into powder and we were faced with the purchase of a new one. This often meant a period of comparative darkness because we seldom had a spare. "What is a 'mantle'" you say? It was a little white meshwork of the shape and size of the container part of an eggcup which, when in contact with the gas flame, was transformed into an incandescent beacon which was brilliantly and beautifully white. This was a magical transformation to my childish mind and I often wondered why a comparatively dull and flickering flame should be altered in this way simply by contact with a little white cup. I realised that there was some-

Chapter One: First Evidence

thing special in the constitution of the mantle and I remember reading the label on the empty mantle box to find out what it was.

Even now I can see the wording in my mind's eye: "contains oxides of the rare earths thorium and cerium" it said. I supposed (correctly as it turned out) that it was these substances which incandesced whiter than white when in contact with a hot flame. But at the time it used to puzzle me why any earth should be called "rare". There was certainly a lot of earth, of many different sorts, around where I lived. There was so much of it that it got everywhere, much to the chagrin of my mother who was frequently faced with the problem of washing it off the skin and clothing of small boys. Washday itself was something of an epic procedure. Always on a Monday, it consisted of boiling the sheets and other white cotton articles in a coal-fired boiler in the corner of a little annexe called the "scullery". The boiler itself was conveniently adjacent to the dull yellow, rectangular and shallow, sink with its single brass cold tap. There was no question of hot water coming out of a tap in those days, and in that society. I had reached my teens before I realised that sometimes it did.

The scullery was a single storied affair which appeared to be an afterthought fitting to the house itself. Contiguous with the scullery but with no access from indoors was the outside lavatory. This was a water closet with a trade mark just below the water vent. "*Adamant Patent*" it said and I occasionally wondered if it was the original design used by Adam in the Garden of Eden. Such is the evocative power of words to make connections in the childish mind. You will notice that I specify a "water closet". This is because in those days there were still houses, especially in country districts, which had earth closets. I remember using such fixtures myself on visits to friends and relations. The waste from such closets was periodically removed by the "ten o'clock horsemen" and I will leave you to work out the significance of the name yourself. There were many jokes about the horsemen, none of which I could possibly repeat in these sanitised times.

The Sceptical Witness

During the winter months the outside water closet tended to freeze up unless we prevented this by placing a lighted candle adjacent to where the water pipe emerged from the floor. This was the only time there was any form of installed illumination for visits to the closet at night, although the nervous could take their own candle, or perhaps a paraffin lamp, if they wished to do so. I remember being perpetually surprised that such a small source of heat as a candle could successfully prevent the pipe from freezing, particularly when the water closet door had a six inch gap both top and bottom. The candle certainly had no noticeable effect on the freezing effect of the lavatory seat on adolescent buttocks. The fact that the candle was such an effective frost guard is an illustration of the general law that a small constraint placed in exactly the right location exercises an effect altogether out of proportion to the constraint itself. I later came to realise that such is true of all aspects of human life, and not only the physical ones.

The gap under the door had its uses apart from ventilation. If one wished to see if the closet was occupied it was only necessary to kneel down in the back yard and squint under the door. Of course, had I referred to the closet at the time I would have called it the "lavatory" rather than the "closet" because the latter word was used only by those considered to be socially somewhat inferior. Yes, the English working class of the nineteen twenties and thirties was riddled with class distinction in small, but immensely important, things. Social stratification was evident then as it is in all societies, in all lands, at all times. Personally I always considered the use of the word "closet" to be slightly daring and I would certainly never have used it within the hearing of my mother. Perhaps this restraint was associated with a variant of an old song which we urchins regularly used to sing when we were free of parental influence.

Chapter One: First Evidence

Old King Cole was a merry old soul
and a merry old soul was he
He called for a light in the middle of the night
and he went to the WC
The Moon shone on the closet seat and the candle had a fit
Old King Cole fell down the hole and .....

And you may now use your imagination to complete the doggerel if you feel so inclined. Our own last lines varied somewhat according to the linguistic inventiveness of the singer.

But back to the washing. The small back yard was virtually a no-go area on a Monday morning when the sheets were hung out to dry and they seemed to take up every inch of available space. The sheets had previously been boiled, washed, rinsed and "mangled". The mangle was a large wringer made totally of cast iron with the exception of two enormous wooden rollers. The procedure was to remove the sheets from the boiling copper with a stout laundry stick and to drop them into the "dolly tub" where they were given a thorough pounding in hot water with yellow washing soap by means of an instrument known as a "ponch". The ponch itself was a substantial feat of joinery made out of pine wood and consisting of a heavy object which looked like an inverted flowerpot with a hemispherical instead of a flat bottom. This was partly hollow and the internal cavity was joined to the exterior by four equally spaced slots to allow the water to flow in and out during the pounding action. A waist-high stick joined the business end of the ponch to a crosspiece handle which, gripped by small boys, allowed them to ponch (the word was also a verb) the washing until allowed to go and play. I remember that my first murder case many years later involved a ponch used as a weapon of assault. However being in Yorkshire and not in Nottinghamshire it was referred to as a "posser". The nuances of the two dialects doubtless escaped the unfortunate victim.

I shared a bedroom with my middle brother and we slept on iron bedsteads. There was a small fire grate in the room but it was quite useless. On the few occasions we attempted to light a fire in it more smoke was vented into the bedroom than passed up the chimney. On frosty days the temperature was often below freezing point in the bedroom and I recall the chamber pot under the bed being frozen on several occasions. Likewise the moisture in the breath from two young sleeping bodies would, throughout a winter night, condense on to the inside of the window pane and freeze into a series of incredibly beautiful foliar patterns. It was one of my pleasures on winter mornings to lie in bed and to see how many different leaves I could count. We all believed that if the windows were touched sharply when these frozen patterns were present then the window would disintegrate into a million crystalline particles. We never had the nerve to experiment. A broken window would have been a major financial tragedy had the landlord refused to repair it under the heading of "fair wear and tear".

The sounds and smells of childhood are still with me and, a common experience amongst the elderly, they become more vivid with the passage of time. The clank of the measure as it was hooked on to the side of the can by the milkman after dispensing our family pint into a waiting jug. The sharp whistle of the baker on the pavement outside the house as he called his horse from its previous stop. The horse would come immediately and it knew exactly where to stop. Most of the distance covered by a deliveryman's horse and dray in those days seemed to be done without a driver, the horse knew exactly what was expected of it. I suppose that the facility will be re-invented some day in the form of a robot and hailed as a huge success for science. There was also a hawker selling water cress who came by regularly but my mother never bought anything from him. She maintained it was gathered from a stream draining a swamp near the local colliery. I think she was right. Perhaps the original streams of the Nottingham Meadows had once been replete with the wholesome weed growing in crystal clear running water but those days were long gone. As the river meadows gave way to the advance of terraced housing and colliery spoil heaps, it seemed that the only streams left were doomed to start or finish in a swamp, at the base of some pile of industrial waste.

Chapter Two: Early Investigations

My education started at the age of three when I went to nursery school with my brother, then aged five. In truth five was the minimum age for entry but I made so much fuss to go with my brother that my mother gave in and prevailed upon the headmistress to take me. My teachers were, at different times, Miss Fletcher and Miss Chester and the headmistress was Mrs Adams. Mrs Adams always wore dark brown dresses and did her hair in a bun. The similarity between "Adams" and "Adam" together with the biblical overtones of the name, and the lady's undoubted authority, confused her identity in my childish mind with that of God. The teaching was simple and plainly Christian. We used to sing:

Jesus bids us shine with a pure clear light
Like a little candle burning in the night
In this world of darkness so we must shine
You in your small corner, and I in mine.

which has always seemed to me a straightforward injunction of much value in a society of swiftly changing values or none.

At Christmas we were all encouraged to write to Santa Claus and the letters produced were then despatched in the traditional way by burning them and coaxing the carbonised sheets up the chimney. On one occasion I remember going out into the playground to find it full of noisy children, busy catching the floating black flakes and crushing them in an orgy of destruction. I pointed out to the teacher that crumbling the messages was not going to render Santa Claus's task any easier, but she assured me that such difficulties made no problems for the saint, he just knew what was written. I remember feeling unconvinced. I even considered searching for my own carbonised contribution to protect it, but since I had no idea what to do with it when I found it, I decided not to. Considering this incident after so many years perhaps it illustrates a general principle. If you have no idea what to do yourself, perhaps you should accept the word of your seniors.

The Sceptical Witness

Politics was early a part of my life in that my brother and I sometimes accompanied our parents to Labour Party meetings. My father was the local ward secretary. These meetings were usually held in St George's Church hall, and during the meeting, my brother and I played quietly on the gymnasium equipment stacked at the back of the hall. On one occasion I witnessed a disturbance in a meeting when an occupant of a seat on the front row was accused of harassment because he was persistently pointing at the speaker. In the end the trouble-maker was summarily ejected. My father often used to tell the story thereafter with great amusement because it transpired that all the heckler was trying to do was indicate to the speaker that his fly-buttons were undone. This is another incident which has coloured my ideas on the nature of "justice".

Religion was a constant companion. My parents were ambivalent in the matter but I and my brother had been baptised into the Church of England and we were encouraged to attend Sunday school. Nevertheless we were allowed a good deal of freedom in deciding which to attend and so we experienced the Church of England, the Congregationalists, the Wesleyan Methodists and the Salvation Army. The last was our favourite and I even advanced to the stage of playing the euphonium in the junior band, although my brother avoided such commitments. Bible class on a Sunday morning at the Salvation Army was a good disciplinary preamble to our expeditions into the countryside, before Sunday dinner. Mischief was a regular element of these Sunday mornings and one occasion rests in my mind almost as vividly as on the day it occurred.

I had become the proud possessor of a blank cartridge starting pistol, a type of appliance freely available to children in those days. This was a single shot device which fired .22" calibre cartridges with a resounding crack. One Sunday I took this to bible class with me, comfortably secreted and loaded, in my pocket. The bible class that morning was in the charge of a nervous young student bible teacher, in her early teens. Her gift of entrancing the young with wonderful stories from the Bible was no match for the provocative feel of the pistol butt in my

Chapter Two: Early Investigations

pocket. We sat there on wooden forms in the main hall. At one end of the hall was the stage and in front of this was the bench at which supplicants knelt to be saved. I had been saved there several times myself but, after this morning, I was never saved again. Along the back of this bench in large red and gold letters was the legend "Blood and Fire", a message that I felt was somehow strangely apposite and stimulating.

There were probably a dozen bible classes under way in the hall, each on a pair of benches one of which had been turned to face the other. A low buzz of voices and the rustle of turning bible pages provided the background as, bored to desperation, I removed the pistol from my pocket and stuck it into the abdomen of my brother who sat facing me on the opposite bench. A moment's consternation showed on his face but it was quickly followed by a sardonic expression which said quite plainly "you wouldn't dare!" But I did dare, and I pulled the trigger. Then I put the pistol back into my pocket and awaited the outcome. In the enclosed space the report of the pistol seemed like the explosion of a bomb and there followed a long moment of silence as all the voices in the hall abruptly ceased. The white face of our young teacher mirrored the shock of all those present, save me, as the good and gentle stories of the Bible were suddenly supplanted by the seeming advent of judgement day.

In fact judgement day did not arrive, but the Songster Master did. He was a large and magnificent figure in his navy blue uniform and white cord epaulettes (the Band Master wore red ones) and he approached our terrified teacher, having unerringly identified the class from which the explosion had come. "Which one is it?" said the Songster Master. The teacher, incapable of speech, indicated my brother with a shaking finger, as the general direction from which the shot had come. Without further preamble the Songster Master picked up my brother, and another boy who was sitting next to him, each by the scruff of the neck and marched them unceremoniously down to the main door where he threw them out.

The Sceptical Witness

I sat there with my hands folded primly on my lap staring straight ahead with my face bearing as uninvolved an expression as I could muster. The footsteps of the Songster Master approached me from behind and passed by on his way to the front of the hall. I gently began to release a sigh of relief as his huge figure receded towards the stage. Alas my deliverance was only temporary. Armed with the experience of one who had lived through the teeming factory sweatshops of the late nineteenth century and the horrors of the first world war, and uninhibited by the dicta of late 20th century apologists for naughty children, he suddenly stopped, turned, and looked directly at me. For a moment he seemed almost undecided. Then his expression hardened and he reapproached the class. "I think we'll have this one too" he said. Then he threw me out as well. Life had taught him not to rely entirely upon eyewitness identification.

A typical working class child of the time I built crystal wireless sets, made model aeroplanes, electric motors and complicated *Meccano* constructions. Outdoors I picnicked and camped regularly and I fished and swam in the Trent. Thinking about it I cannot remember any of my friends who did not fish in the Trent. It seemed to be part of the natural order of things, like walking and sleeping. Everyone seemed to start the same way, with a piece of bamboo cane, some sewing thread, a bent pin and some damp bread which was thoroughly kneaded to provide the stiff paste which, rolled into tiny balls, provided the bait. We caught only minnows this way although we called them "struts", the name "minnows" being reserved for the small fry.

Some of us graduated to three-piece rods with proper silk fishing lines, lead weights and barbed hooks. Our bait became more sophisticated and we used earthworms, maggots, creed wheat and boiled hemp seed. The real *cognoscenti* tended to carry maggots in their mouths, between the lower lip and the teeth, because they said it rendered the maggots more attractive to the fish. These fishermen were admired but seldom emulated by the majority. The day I received my first fishing reel is still clear in my memory. It was a present from my uncle, a bachelor brother of my father. "Present" did I say? Well not exactly. What he actually gave me was the pawn ticket and I saved my pocket money to redeem the reel. Fishing gear was practically legal tender then. I kept the reel as a souvenir through much of my adult life until it became lost in one of the numerous house moves my job demanded. Once, far away from Nottingham, I showed the reel to a fishing enthusiast friend and he immediately recognised it as a "Nottingham reel". Apparently it was a design peculiar to my home town and I remember feeling inordinately proud that my birthplace bore such a distinction.

We caught only coarse fish such as gudgeon, roach and tench. The heyday of the Trent as a salmon river was long past. Although small boys seemed to thrive on swimming in the Trent it was much too polluted for the prince of fishes. Discussing the question of river pollution many years later with a forensic scientist colleague he humorously commented that the Trent may have been polluted but it was not as bad as his own home river, the Tyne. This, he maintained, had the distinction of being the only river in the world in which it was impossible to drown. When we children were not fishing we tended to go exploring a large area of wasteland which was bordered on one side by the river, on another by a colliery and elsewhere by a railway line and the local Royal Ordnance Factory. Each of these sections of the perimeter yielded its own enchantments for the growing mind. The colliery furnished mounds of shale (locally known as 'bat') for us to imagine as mountains in far-off lands. Adjacent to these mountains was a swampy wasteland of rushes and sedges called "Cheggy's Field" which provided us with imagined tropical jungles to explore, and bleeding wounds where the razor sharp sedges lacerated our bare knees. If the sedges didn't draw blood the leeches often did. "Bloodsuckers" we called them, which is probably a better name than "leeches".

I believed, until quite recently, that "Cheggy's" was the name of a previous owner because "Cheggy" was the local nickname for a left-handed person. Later I came to the view that it was more likely a corruption of a fairly common English field name "Checker's Field", a field with patchy coloured soil. If that was the true origin of the name it was no longer relevant. Spoil heaps and blocked field drains had generated a rich swamp vegetation through which the soil was quite invisible.

For the adventurous child there was the occasional pit pony to ride bare-back. For the heroic there was an old crane in the river docks which provided a ninety foot high climb, in and out of box girders, and a slide down another girder to the control cabin, now sealed, as the age of the river barges came to an end. I never tried it myself. I have always possessed the twin survival assets of cowardice and a vivid imagination. These allowed me to see what the result would look like had I fallen. We built fires from the waste scraps of coal on the colliery heaps, and we built make-believe houses out of fragments of old timber and corrugated iron. Sometimes we manufactured "winter-warmers" which were a sort of home-constructed censer made out of well-pierced tin cans secured to the end of long loops of wire. Stuffed with small pieces of coal gleaned from the colliery tip, they were carefully ignited with bits of old wood and newspaper and then swung around our heads until they became fiery satellites. Sometimes the standards of design and engineering did not match the high temperature and the generated G-forces which stressed the wire handle, and then the white hot can became detached and flew off at a tangent to scatter its contents widely over the waste land where we played. "Fowler's Field" it was called, although Fowler, if he existed, had so long departed to meet his maker that no-one seemed to remember him. Or perhaps the name was the last remaining evidence of a pre-enclosure great swampy field frequented by hunters with their long fowling pieces. In any case all resemblance to a "field" had long since disappeared under the layers of colliery waste and other miscellaneous rubbish.

No, that was not entirely true. There was still one oasis of green in the grey waste and this was provided by the colliery football field, which was surrounded on all sides by embankments of colliery spoil, through one of which penetrated a tunnel which provided access to the pitch. There, in this curiously protected environment, was the last relict of a beautiful oddity, the days when the Nottingham Meadows blossomed in Spring with acres of the blue spring crocus. It was said, though long before my time, that there were so many crocuses then that they gave

Chapter Two: Early Investigations

the impression of having been planted as a crop. Of the ones left in my childhood, around the edges of the football field, many fell to the raids of armies of urchins who were intent on brightening their mothers' lives with large bunches of a flower which, elsewhere in England, grew only in gardens. Thirty years later I was to spot an emblem of a single blue spring crocus on the tie of a senior police officer. It proved that he was a Nottingham man and the tie was that of the Nottingham Criminal Investigation Department of which he had, some years before, been a member. But we must go back sixty years in time, and twenty paces in space, through the colliery tunnel, and once more we are back on the grey waste of Fowler's Field. To my childish mind Fowler's had always been a wide and mysterious wonderland that, particularly on misty days, became a place of enchantment. I think it was on Fowler's Field that there first surfaced in my mind the desire to see what lay beyond. Beyond what? Beyond any limiting barrier, be it a commonly held belief, a corner, a description decayed in time to a name, a swathe of fog, a corrugated iron fence, a railway embankment, the barrier to sight of microscopic size or the obstacle of human stupidity.

I remember conversations with friends on the possible existence of fairies in some form of the beyond and, one morning on Fowler's Field, a friend and I debated whether there might be some of the small creatures in the mist, on the wasteland, beyond our field of vision. My accomplice suggested that we should dispose of the matter, there and then, by going to see. I readily agreed but pointed out that, should we find none, that was not proof that there hadn't been some just before we arrived. Being an intensely practical individual my friend changed his mind about the investigation and decided that his time could be much better spent elsewhere. He was not interested in philosophical quibbles. Life for him was to be lived and only to be thought about to the extent that happiness demanded. He went off to play marbles instead. I still have many friends who think like him and I am beginning to suspect that they may all be right.

The Sceptical Witness

A similar critical discussion with my contemporaries dealt with the method of human reproduction as it had been described to us by older boys. In this case we finally decided the matter by concluding that babies formed spontaneously in the bodies of their mothers. We felt that the alternative which had been described to us was so bizarre that it lacked all credibility. I still maintain a trace of this view.

This was my mental world throughout my early life until I left school at the age of fourteen. The habit of withdrawing into such reveries did not pass unnoticed by my teachers and on one occasion, when I was about nine years old, my teacher asked my mother to call at the school to see her. It appeared, so my mother told me afterwards, that the teacher was concerned that I lived in a world of my own. At least I appeared to do so when she addressed questions to me in class. The poor lady was doubtless right because I was usually under the impression that my thoughts were much more interesting than her lessons. She suggested to my mother that perhaps a visit to the psychiatrist was in order but, happily, my mother ignored the advice. I shudder to think of what a nineteen-thirties psychiatrist might have prescribed as treatment for a preoccupied and dreamy nine year old. It was the same teacher who, giving a lesson on elementary geology, told us the story of how the chalk cliffs of England were deposited millions of years ago in the form of the shells of microscopic marine creatures which, in consolidated form, gave us the chalk measures of today. To illustrate the point, I remember, she dramatically held aloft a stick of blackboard chalk and told us that if we examined it under the microscope we would be able to see all those tiny creatures which had lived so long ago.

Later in life, when I first gained access to a microscope, I tried to view these microscopic organisms on several occasions without success, until further reading and enquiry informed me that blackboard chalk was not natural chalk but a quite different compound. To paraphrase a long dead popular philosopher "It all depends on what you mean by 'chalk'". I now prefer to believe that my teacher stood in greater need of a geologist than I did of a psychiatrist. Perhaps it was my self ab-

Chapter Two: Early Investigations

sorption which caused, and still causes, a certain dour facial expression to be my lot. When one spends a lot of time in the mental world it is sometimes difficult to keep outward appearances in mind. I can only remember one occasion when I made a determined attempt to appear more cheerful to the outside world and it ended in abject failure. I was about ten at the time and, with the children of several other schools, was taking part in rehearsals for a children's massed choir rendition of Tannhäuser.

My school was led into the auditorium first which meant I was in the centre of the front row and had to sit upon the floor whilst the other schools were led in behind us and got the comfortable seats. When we were all there (there were hundreds of us) the conductor who had been waiting at the front said he wanted to see the joyful occasion reflected in the smiles upon our faces. I dutifully complied and, with all the determination at my command, adopted a resolutely joyful expression which must have lasted for several hundred bars of Wagner. It was a performance every bit as heroic as the Tannhäuser itself and although my face began to ache I doggedly persisted and kept a fixed and jubilant expression in place as I gritted out the words through lips drawn hard back against my teeth.

When stars above in myriads shine
O'er all the earth so calm and fair
It fills the soul with longing deep
That we on earth were also there...

I think that the conductor began to wish he was there too and he finally gave up, and signalled for silence. Then he said to the entire assembly. "There is a boy sitting on the front row wearing the ghastly leer of a village idiot, and I don't think I can stand it much longer". Any doubts about the object of his comments were dispelled when the boy sitting next to me stuck his elbow in my ribs and hissed "he means you!". I was appalled by the conductor's behaviour. He had asked for a joyful expression and he got one. Then he behaved so ungratefully. I don't think I've ever tried to look joyful since.

The Sceptical Witness

Which mental capacities are inborn and which are learned? The nature of proof was obviously part of my mental universe of discourse even in those far gone days (witness the fairies tale) although the idea of cause and effect remained naively straightforward for me for a long time afterwards. Yes, I realise the two ideas of proof and cause are closely connected and perhaps are just two aspects of the same basic reality, but the demands of practical living and practical thinking require that our routine daily and our mental lives be carved up into recognisable chunks. Everything may be connected to everything else in this world but we can only think about it a bit at a time. Or perhaps we do think about it all each time, but only from one standpoint.

Much that will be useful to the child later in life must be learned by rote. "Discovery" methods of teaching have proved a disaster and this is well illustrated by the supermarket checkout assistant who is capable only of pointing to the till readout and is unable to see that five items, each less than a pound each, can hardly total more than six pounds. At our school we learned our tables by chanting them from one-times-one to twelve-times-twelve as we marched into school for the morning assembly. This gave even the unable a useful accomplishment and it enabled the dreamers to have an anchor to reality to steady them as they meandered along the byways of the intellect.

Once arrived in assembly we stood in serried and silent obedience as school notices were read, the occasional public caning was administered to the really recalcitrant, the daily hymn was sung and finally the *Nunc Dimittis* was thankfully rendered:

Oh Lord, now lettest thy servant depart in peace according to thy word
For mine eyes have seen thy salvation
Which has been a light to lighten the Gentiles
and to be the glory of thy people Israel
Glory be to the Father and to the Son
and to the Holy Ghost
As it was in the beginning is now and ever shall be
World without end, Aaaaaaaaamen.

Chapter Two: Early Investigations

If it happened that the first class of the day, after assembly, was mathematics with Mr McGough, then we stood in need of as much spiritual strength as we could get. He always welcomed us into his class in the same way. "Boys, when you pass across the golden doorstep you move from the noise and tumult of the world at large into the peace and quietness beyond". We did too. Maccy had a habit of emphasising his words for the benefit of the slow witted by beating the desk gently with his constant companion, a two thonged leather strap. Other teachers might have tolerated a modest degree of indiscipline but not Maccy. Boys came to his class to be educated in the subject of mathematics and educated in the subject of mathematics they most certainly would be.

It was obvious that he recognised the varying abilities of different members of the human race but he plainly considered this fact as no more than God's challenge to his teaching skill. His attitude rubbed off on to the boys too. Our class contained boys who, in more "enlightened" times, might have been classified as "disturbed" and given special treatment in a class with their intellectual peers but here they were just accepted as a part of the situation that prevailed, a microcosm of society, a unit of a fellowship. Put simply, Maccy treated them equally but differently. Sadly it would not work nowadays. Maccy's method of teaching would not pass muster in the caring seminaries of the modern world. He was a very good teacher but, oh heinous crime!, he used fear as one of his teaching methods. It was the experience of fear, mixed with respect, in Maccy's classroom which taught me the many elementary mathematical elements and techniques that I found so useful in later life.

I refer to those abilities which allow one to recognise mathematical nonsense in all the aspects of daily life, ranging from the economic pronouncements of politicians to the contrivances of that minority of publicans, shopkeepers and salesmen who look upon society exclusively as an agency for enhancing their individual prosperities. Amongst the many mathematical resources that Maccy taught me and my fellows was the *Rule of Signs*. Since that lesson I have never forgotten the rule but, intriguingly, I can never dissociate it from the particular lesson which imparted it.

What is the *Rule of Signs*? The rule is of basic importance in mathematics and it is of prime significance, *inter alia*, in the design of computer systems. It is one of those basic elements of logic which pervade our lives whether we recognise them as such or no. Laws of this type are not truths of fact but truths of reason. One doesn't discover them by experiment, or stumble across them by serendipity. One works them out by means of the spongy tissue located midway between the two ears. Ruminating about such things gives the habitual thinker, whatever his personal capacity as such, an enormous pleasure of the same potency as that stimulated by all great works of art and nature. Whatever the opinion of Mr McGough in such matters he had the grasp of a good teacher who is faced by the problem of teaching abstract ideas to young minds in that he started by giving us concrete examples. "Let us imagine" he said "that I have decided to give you all a half day's holiday this afternoon. The cheer which followed was cut short by the sudden realisation that one did not cheer in Maccy's class. "Let us further imagine", he said, "that the headmaster in his wisdom has reversed my decision and has decided that you cannot have the holiday". The ensuing groan was likewise cut short.

He followed this example with the remaining three possibilities: teacher no/headmaster yes, teacher yes/headmaster yes, teacher no/headmaster no.

"So we see in the general case", said Mr McGough "that the headmaster makes a decision about my decision. When my decision and that of the headmaster are at variance then you don't get a holiday. When they are in agreement then you do, even" here he paused "when the head says no to my decision that you don't get a holiday".

He obviously knew that he might be losing some of the class at this stage but, time being short, he went on to enunciate the general case. Positive times negative equals negative. Negative times positive equals negative. Positive times positive equals positive and negative times negative equals positive.

"We shall now proceed to see how much of that you have grasped" said Mr McGough" moving from behind his desk into the body of the classroom, leather strap in hand. He addressed the first boy.

"Positive times negative?" "No half holiday Sir" replied the boy. "Whack" went the strap. On to the next boy.

"Positive times negative?" "No half holiday Sir" replied the boy. "Whack" went the strap again and Maccy moved on to the third boy.

I watched with fascination as the teacher moved down the line of boys, each one giving an identical answer which, after the first boy, each knew was the incorrect one. Not one made a stab at a different answer. Somehow each had followed the correct line of reasoning until it came to the *pons asinorum*, the bridge from the concrete to the abstract and this they had failed to cross. After seven or eight boys Mr McGough reached me. "Positive times negative?" he enquired. "Negative Sir" I replied. "Correct" said Mr McGough, "take three credits". All the boys in line before me looked at me with surly resentment. All those in line after me looked at me with gratitude. Now, almost sixty years later, I remember the pageant as clearly as I can remember the rule of signs. I can't help but think that most of my classmates remember both too.

"Deplorable teaching practice" did you say? Perhaps so in modern eyes. But how many teachers are held in such great esteem that years after Mr McGough's retirement many of his pupils, now fathers and even grandfathers themselves, regularly took the trouble to travel to a town centre pub in Nottingham to drink with an ageing but evergreen Maccy?

The Sceptical Witness

Chapter Three: Potatoes and Thinking

Thinkers tend to develop the capacity to generalise as they mature, but it seems that their ability to communicate their thoughts to others does not keep pace. Many years after I had considered the possible existence of fairies I wrote a book entitled *"The Scientific Investigation of Crime"*. I thought it was a very good book indeed, and I was convinced it broke new conceptual ground in the field of crime investigation. It also brought me a reasonable amount of money which, after all, is one way to judge the success of a book. Remember what I said about betting on scientific theories? Isn't this an analogous situation?

The police did not think much of the book, the lawyers ignored it and the medicals restricted themselves to picking up proof-reading errors. Only writers and magistrates expressed approval and they thought it was wonderful. What this means, if one searches for a general rule, is that the closer the professional connection with crime investigation, the less were the readers disposed to admit that the book contained anything of value. Was it the fact that, for many professionals, the conceptual and general nature of the background in which their specialty is embedded is a topic they never bother themselves with? And the scientists? From that quarter there was deathly silence. Only once did I ever receive a direct comment from a scientist and that from a friend in my last laboratory. He said "you know Stuart, nobody at the lab understands your book". Oh well, back to the nineteen thirties.

We had a great number of games and occupations during my childhood, all of them, as I remember, quite innocuous if somewhat noisy. One of these was our enrolling into "gangs". Menacing though this may sound, all that was involved was the production of highly recondite secret signs and passwords, arcane languages, concealed messages and the organisation of furtive meetings. The agenda in such meetings was limited to elaborating mysterious schemes, producing cryptic bulletins and organising further meetings. Most members immediately forgot the decisions taken at these meetings so that any particular gang lasted only a few days before it was consigned to the rubbish bin of unremembered fraternities. Adult political parties seem to adhere to the same pattern, but with a rather longer time scale.

The Sceptical Witness

But there were longer established habits and practices in our community memories. Of the many pavement games we played in the nineteen twenties and thirties there was one called "Jiggy horses, belly horses" and this is a good example of a long lasting "folk" memory. The game simply consisted of roping each other together in a long line and imagining ourselves to be horses, with the last urchin in line as the driver. Thereafter we charged up and down the pavement at high speed, shouting our heads off and infuriating the local populace, particularly those working on night shift. It is only recently that I have come to realise that we were playing a degenerate version of a game that must have been very popular in the eighteenth and nineteenth centuries, the heyday of the pack horse. Packhorses were often termed jaggers. The lead jagger in the packhorse train wore bells and was called the "bell horse"; hence "jiggy horses, belly horses". We had no idea of these origins in the nineteen thirties and no packhorse train would have lasted more than a few minutes at the speed and energy of our childish bodies.

Most evidence in any historical investigation, be it the origin of children's games, the origin of field names or the search for a serial killer, exists in a layered form. Each of these layers encloses a diminished form of the evidence which is contained in the layer beneath. It is the business of the investigator, in whatever field, to dig to the lowest and most accurate level, free of the irrelevancies contained in the overburden. It is in some respects rather like the excavations of an archaeologist, although this is an analogy that should not be pushed too far. A good example of this intellectual digging is illustrated by an incident late in my career as a forensic scientist. I was involved in a long running series-murder investigation and this led me to attempt to reconstruct a useful name from a possibly false one given by an assailant to his intended victim in an attempted murder. The situation was complicated by the victim's injuries and her resulting confusion over what the assailant had actually said to her.

Keeping in mind that false names used by criminals often have some connection with the user or his associates, there were certain aspects to the case which allowed me, mentally, to dig down through the layers and come up with a plausible name and address to check. I made my suggestion to the investigating officer and he went ahead and did the check. This I felt was particularly important since the individual I named lived very near the focus of certain other police enquiries in this particular case. But the man I named proved to be a retired school teacher who, at a certain moment which was evidentially critical, had been in a hospital intensive care unit suffering from a heart attack. Thus he could not have been the individual whom the police were looking for. Disappointed I turned to other aspects of the investigation which proved to be more fruitful.

When subsequently discussing this incident, after the investigation was completed and the series killer convicted, one of my colleagues pointed out to me that there was a good chance that the killer had been taught by this particular schoolmaster and had chosen his teacher's name as a convenient cover. So in a sense perhaps I was right. If so the information might have been of some, if limited, value had it been realised at the time. Perhaps I stopped digging one layer too soon. But all such speculations must be viewed, in the practical context, against a background of many lines of enquiry competing for limited resources. Be that as it may, all good investigators know that by turning over commonplace facts in the mind some useful leads may result. It may not be evidence of the type that one can use in court but it could well lead to the discovery of such evidence. Crime investigation is the science of the commonplace and the commonplace is layered.

Back in the thirties I started work at the age of twelve when I went to work part-time on a Co-op horse-drawn greengrocery van. I worked Friday nights and Saturdays mornings. The Friday night sessions were pretty local to where I lived but the Saturday morning round was in north Nottingham and it was this expedition that I liked best of all. We started at six in the morning in the greengrocery loading bay. The cart was ready backed into the bay in the position we had left it the previous night. We did all our own loading and it used to take us about half an hour, which time included fetching Coleen the horse. Coleen was a beautiful, sleek, black vanner (a small carthorse) mare of uncertain temperament and I was rather afraid of her. I always thought that she tended to look at me in a speculative fashion and I tried to be out of sight working on the roof of the van when the time came to hitch her up. Happily my help was not always necessary because there would be other drivers present and ready to give a hand. I've been a little afraid of horses ever since I met Coleen but I try not to show it, particularly when I'm with my granddaughter Rachael and her Shetland pony.

Sacks of sprouts, onions and carrots went on to the van roof together with boxes of apples, oranges, dates, pomegranates and hosts of other things. Down below, open boxes of produce were neatly arranged in two sloping banks, one facing left and the other right. A good deal of trouble was taken by my driver to arrange the display in as attractive a fashion as possible, an endeavour which paid dividends because he was nearly always the top salesman in the greengrocery department. An exception to the neatly sloping display was made for the potatoes which were kept at the back of the cart in two open sacks, one containing King Edwards and the other holding Whites. The Whites were always the cheaper of the two. Adjacent to the potatoes was the spring balance which, when we were under way, was hooked around the nearside rear corner upright. It was also here that I had my seat on the ride out and the ride home.

The ride out was always an uneventful trot on the flat and a steady walk up the hills, of which there were three. Horse drawn traffic was still commonplace in those days and the main roads in the city, at least those with any slope, were still surfaced with granite cobbles to provide a better footing for the horses. The cobbles made a very noisy combination with traditional metal rimmed wheels, but our cart was a more modern one and it had pneumatic tyres and drum brakes. This made the brakes much more effective than those which worked simply by levering a block against a metal wheel rim. The only sounds when the cart was in motion was the steady clip clop of Coleen's hooves and the regular sway and creaking of the cart and the rubbing together of the boxes of merchandise. It was a very superior cart. During the

Chapter Three: Potatoes and Thinking

daily round itself Coleen wore a horse coat. Made of waterproof canvas on the outside, it had a soft and fleecy blanket on the inside. Moreover, when the time came to go home the coat, now comfortably hot from Coleen's body heat, was wrapped around my waist and bare knees as I sat at the back of the cart among the potatoes. It gave me a feeling of exquisite comfort which I have seldom experienced since. Coleen always knew when home time was approaching and she became restive. Left to herself she would have cut out the final few customers on the round and headed straight for home on her own. So it was always necessary to make sure the brakes were well applied at each of our late stops.

And what a ride home. The final customer lived a hundred yards from the main road out of Notttingham to the North and it was on to this road that we had to turn, across the stream of traffic, to travel south to the city. It was a hair raising start. Because the brake was full on Coleen had no chance of pulling away before the driver let her go but, once he had picked his moment, off went the brake and off went Coleen across the traffic stream with an enormous snatch which would have thrown me off the back of the cart had I not been ready for it. The junction where we started was at the top of the first of three hills and we were soon going downhill at a cracking pace with Coleen held to a steady canter and with the cart rolling from side to side to the rhythm of her movement. This continued to the bottom of the first hill where we then started to climb the second. Coleen and the cart, half a ton of the first and two tons of the second, gradually slowed to a trotting pace and then to a walk. With the inertia of herself and the cart now fully spent it was necessary to pull hard to get up the hill and by now she was pretty well warmed up.

If it was a cold winter's day it was at this spot that the steam began to rise from her glossy black back. After half a mile or so, with the uphill pull completed, Coleen went over the top and speeded up again until she was cantering steadily downhill all the way to the bottom of the slope and then part way up the other side where she slowed once more to a trot, and then to a walk, for the longer pull up to the top of the third and last hill. Then it happened. This was it. A mile long run down a slope to the old flood plain of the Trent and the Meadows and, for Coleen, the final run on the flat to the stables, a comfortable stall and a full manger. Nothing could have stopped her from then on. I am sure a fully applied brake would have had no other effect than to leave black tyre marks all the way down the cobbled slope to where the flat valley bottom began.

It was the Nottingham Wells Fargo. Two and a half tons of horse, wagon, greengrocery and human beings speeding down the hill. Pedestrians and motor vehicles, more aware of the need to give way to horse flesh in those days, submissively paused or slowed down to allow Coleen's triumphal progress. It was all against the rules of course, and probably against the law, but no-one complained at the magnificent sight of Coleen and cart, with her driver, Don, a tall, lean and weathered figure, standing on the base of the shafts with the reins held casually between his fingers, a Players cigarette hanging nonchalantly from his lips. It was poetry in motion at fifteen miles an hour. I doubt if the speed was much more than that but it felt and looked like fifty. Pedestrians stopped to look and to cheer and, at the few road junctions, motor cars pulled up and waited patiently almost as if enjoined to do so by imaginary traffic lights which certainly did not exist then.

I've often relived those speedy downhill journeys in later life in my imagination. Sometimes I have injected hypothetical happenings into them. One of my favourites is to consider what would have happened if one of the errant and tangential potatoes, which often departed from the cart at this stage, had caused the death, directly or indirectly, of a passer by? Just imagine any one of a multitude of circumstances in which, had such a victim been found dead on the pavement (in the total absence of eye witnesses) with a cracked skull and associated bruising. What would the police have made of it? What would the pathologist have been able to say to the investigating officer? What would the forensic scientist have reported? (Yes, there was a laboratory in Nottingham in those early days). Would he have found traces of raw potato on the victim? What conclusions would he have drawn?

Chapter Three: Potatoes and Thinking

The last mile and a half was dead flat and Don let Coleen have her head. Usually she was content to walk for the first mile but the last half-mile, so close to home, stimulated her to a final gallop to the stables where, released from the shafts and once again wearing her coat, she crossed the windy yard to her stable to await the attention of the stableman. Cool and dried down she finally received her water and oats. What a lovely memory. What a lovely horse. I wish I hadn't been so afraid of her, I think we could have been great friends.

In 1939 I left school at the age of 14. Throughout much of my life I've often considered this to be the greatest mistake I've ever made. I had qualified for Mundella, the local grammar school, but my parents gave me the choice of going there or of going out to work. In truth it would probably have been difficult for me had I elected to go to Mundella at the age of fourteen because of the three year gap in my education. I had been qualified for transfer since the age of eleven but I had chosen not to go during this time and my parents had let me have my way. Because of this long gap any later transfer would have meant that I had to make up for the ground lost during three years of more modest level teaching. A mistake not to go did I say? Well, later in life I began to think that it had, after all, been the right decision. The reason is this. Throughout our lives we absorb the knowledge necessary for life either by precept or by practice. Good education is a mixture of both of these but the best education cannot reproduce the conditions of a busy life lived in developing, and often unforeseen, situations. To some extent we must remain students, educating ourselves and putting ourselves in the way of being educated to absorb new attitudes and skills which enable us to cope with the developing world as it is.

Those in the business of solving real problems soon learn that each problem is, at least in detail, quite unique and that although we must teach ourselves to form general views these must be sufficiently flexible to accommodate the variety of the real world. Facts must take precedence over theory and it is unacceptable to distort, or to be selective about, information which upsets our preconceptions. Few politicians ever learn this lesson.

The Sceptical Witness

Education is wonderful. It provides us with the means to see real cause and effect amongst a host of circumstances where the primitive would see only the deeds of gods and spirits. Education enriches life and permits us to share the thoughts and the discoveries of many intellectual giants who lived long ago and then, armed by these thoughts and discoveries, we may even make our own original mental breakthroughs. But there is, of course, a sense in which education is a disadvantage to the student and that is that it teaches us to search for those patterns in life that our teachers tell us exist. For the most part this means that mental life tends to become a process where facts are fitted into an already patterned mind. Ordinarily this not only doesn't matter but it is the only way we can increase and improve our education. We must take most of what we know, both theory and fact, on trust. We cannot spend our time attempting to build up our intellectual equipment from a mental *tabula rasa*, or blank sheet of intellectual paper, on which we draw our own, personally discovered, picture of the universe. We must take for granted much of what is told us. The products of discovery in any individual human life are modest indeed when compared with the accomplishments of humanity throughout history but the process of discovery, in whatever intellectual field, is a necessity for the fulfilled life.

Consequently the fact that I was precipitated into the real commercial world at the age of 14, and with a limited education, was not completely an instructional disaster. Between 1939 and 1943 I took an assortment of jobs which left me with a medley of skills and experiences, both manual and rational, and of varying utility, which the continuation of a formal education would have denied me. These jobs included cinema projectionist, hatter's assistant, apprentice instrument maker, coal merchant's mate, heavy lorry driver and laboratory assistant. My job as hatter's assistant lasted several months. Located very near to the Old Market Square in Nottingham city centre it gave me an opportunity to study humanity *en masse* during my midday break and it introduced me to the retail business with its, then, strict hierarchical structure. There was a total staff of four: Mr Connolly, Mr Tennyson, Mr Griffin and Mr Kind in strict descending order of sen-

Chapter Three: Potatoes and Thinking

iority. There was no question of familiar forms of address. Upwards addressing required Mr —— and downwards addressing the same but without the prefix. This formality did not mean lack of friendliness or courtesy, indeed both characteristics were much in evidence. It was simply the habit of the times. The firm I worked for was a national chain of hatters, still in business today although with a somewhat changed pattern of merchandise. I can't help thinking that its success might be founded, at least in part, upon its original style of hierarchy and courtesy. In the complex world of cause and effect we still experience today the knock-on effect of what occurred hundreds of years ago. When Henry Ford said "history is bunk" he had, for once, got it wrong.

When I first got the job I was immediately required to buy a hat. One could hardly have the staff leaving the shop, for lunch, hatless. I was fitted out with a remarkably expensive dark green felt hat, for which I was required to pay the cost price. This was a fine piece of headgear and I was secretly very proud of it but it was just not possible for a fourteen year old to return home to a working class district wearing a trilby hat. So I took to carrying a large paper bag. In this I secreted the hat whenever I was anywhere near where I lived. The hat lasted a long time. Indeed for some time I treasured a newspaper photograph of myself at a murder scene wearing the same hat. But that was twenty five years after I bought it, at cost price. Things were built to last in those days.

The job paid about fifteen shillings a week to which I was given the chance to add an extra five shillings by scrubbing the shop floor on a quiet morning during the week if I wished. I wished. Five shillings was a considerable sum and I was not going to pass up such an opportunity. I learned, in the course of time, that the five shillings was the standard allowance for a casual charlady to come in and do the job. The idea that I might be depriving some deserving mother from earning an honest sum did not cross my mind once. Even had it done so I doubt if it would have made any difference. One regular daily job, except on Thursday half day, was to fetch the manager's dinner. This I did by catching a bus at about twelve midday for a three mile journey to the manager's house in a northern suburb of Nottingham. There I was handed, by the managers wife, a flat cardboard box in which, packed in straw, was laid out ready served the manager's dinner. The gravy was supplied separately in a gravy boat (I do not exaggerate) which was required to be kept substantially horizontal in the box during the return journey. This was no mean feat and I was always slightly apprehensive about the moments when I had to step on to, or down from, the bus platform without slopping the gravy.

On my arrival back at the shop I carried the box into the manager's small office where his desk was already laid with cutlery, condiments and a large water jug and tumbler. Presumably I didn't slop the gravy very much because the manager never complained. On the other hand perhaps I did and he chose not to say anything about it. He must have known that it was quite a feat to carry the dinner for three miles on a lurching bus and arrive with it in eatable condition. In the evening he carried the empty box, dishes and the straw home in his voluminous briefcase.

After leaving this job I became an errand boy with the local Coop society, a fact which, upon reaching the age of 16, allowed me to join the Nottingham Co-op platoon of the Home Guard and it gave me my first experience of violence and death. In the early hours of the morning of Friday May 9th, 1941, the City of Nottingham was subjected to a heavy bombing attack by the Luftwaffe. Most of the bombs fell on the Meadows district of the city, possibly as a consequence of the River Trent providing a navigational aid to the German aircraft. It was a frightening experience as our small family crouched in a cubby hole under the stairs, which would have given little if any protection from blast and building collapse had a bomb fallen nearby. We waited and hoped that the next bomb would not find us. I was later to learn that a former classmate, who lived about two hundred yards away, had been killed in the attack.

Chapter Three: Potatoes and Thinking

As the raid slackened I decided to go out and find where the action was and gain some idea of what had happened. In an attempt to give an air of authority to an adolescent who was wandering about the streets of the Nottingham Meadows in the early hours of the morning, I put on my Home Guard uniform and, despite the protestations of my parents, set off. I walked a distance of about two miles, sliding much of the time in my hobnailed boots on a surface of broken glass. Emergency vehicles were audible in the distance and, in the direction of the Home Guard guardroom, there was the dull and flickering glow of burning buildings. On reaching the guardroom I found it empty and so went in search of the duty guard. The guardroom was at the edge of a complex of buildings including the dairy, bakery and stables of the local Co-operative society. I remember wondering if Coleen were still in the stables and if she and the other horses had escaped injury. Several of the buildings were on fire and I walked towards these to see what was happening. It was uncanny. The flickering shadows caused by the flames and the crackle of burning timbers were the only signs of movement and I realised that, since I left home, I had seen no-one on foot. The world seemed deserted and I felt alone at Armageddon.

My loneliness didn't last long. A cry of "hey, youth!" swung me around and I saw the figure of a fireman unrolling a hose coming towards me. "Come with me", he ordered and I followed him to a narrow passageway between two burning single storey buildings. With the hose fully unwound he thrust the long metal nozzle into my hands and told me to keep a tight hold of it while he went to turn on the water. Gripping the hose in the manner I had so often seen on the newsreel at the cinema, or the pictures in the newspapers, I waited for the rush of water, determined that when it came I would not be knocked off my feet. I had in mind the frequent pictures of firemen in the London Blitz where it usually seemed to take two men to control the powerful jet of water and I imagined my shame should the fireman come back and find me trying to retake hold of a writhing nozzle as it lashed around on the floor, sending water everywhere except where it was intended to be.

Burning roofing felt and smoking slates were regularly cascading from the roofs of the two buildings on either side but the hot debris was falling several feet away and I didn't feel threatened. Concentrating on the job in hand I began to imagine boasting of my experiences to my friends the following day when all the excitement was over and I had single-handedly saved the buildings from total destruction.

And gentlemen in England now a-bed
Shall think themselves accursed they were not here,

I waited and my tense arm muscles began to develop cramp. Periodically I cast a quick glance over my shoulder at the long, flat, canvas snake which was the hose. I noticed that in places it was beginning to smoke from the heat and I wondered if, when the water finally arrived, it would only be to spend itself out of a dozen charred holes. But the canvas snake remained resolutely flat and my cramps relentlessly increased. Relief finally came. It seemed as though I had been waiting hours but I don't suppose it could have been more than thirty minutes when the shout came: "You still here youth? You needn't bother, the water main's broken". I felt like hitting the fireman with the nozzle for leaving me holding a useless hose for so long but he was already on his way to duties far more important than mollifying a teenager's hurt feelings. I threw the nozzle down and walked back to the entrance to the alleyway. There I turned and looked at the useless hose, forlornly lying on the paving stones and now well charred and burning in several places. As if to add insult to injury, a long incandescent snake of burning roofing felt and red hot slates now detached itself and ran along the guttering towards me with malevolent intent and increasing speed. I turned and fled.

I went in the same direction as the fireman and came across the guard commander, an elderly corporal, who with several of his men was clearing debris away from an access road. I started to join in but he stopped me and told me to take something to drink to the heavy rescue squad, now working in the bakery which had taken a direct hit. No cold water taps seemed to work so I went back towards the dairy with the

Chapter Three: Potatoes and Thinking

intention of getting some milk. However on the dairy loading platform I saw a stack of crates of something much more refreshing, lemonade. I grabbed two bottles and made my way along the access road being cleared by the Home Guard, into the bakery and then down a track between huge tumbled piles of sacks of flour. Some way inside the bakery the heavy rescue team were working under an arc light half way up a mountain of sacks of flour resting on which was a fallen steel girder. Placing the lemonade firmly on the top of an adjacent sack I began to climb towards the rescue team. One of the team turned towards me. His face was a mask of fatigue as he raised his hand to stop me and then signalled for me to go away. Presumably he thought a weedy teenager would be more trouble than assistance in those circumstances.

I retired some distance and stood watching for a while. The flour sacks were brilliant white under the arc lights except for some widespread black stains. It was not until I had seen them later, in daylight, that I realised that these were stains of blood. This is a lesson that every forensic scientist learns sooner or later. It is far better to search for bloodstains in a softer tungsten filament light than in a brilliant white fluorescent light. The red colour shows up better and they can be differentiated from other stains to a greater degree. But such matters were not to concern me for another ten years. Picking my way through the fallen sacks of flour I made for the exit. On the way I noted another fallen roof section propped up by a heap of flour sacks and, at the bottom of these, protruding between two white sacks, was a white human hand. I told the corporal about this but he already knew. The man was dead. Some days later I went back to this location when my regular turn for guard duty came around. The hand was still there but someone had covered it decorously with an inverted biscuit tin. The safe removal of the collapsed roof, and the recovery of the body, evidently required facilities not immediately available.

The rest of the night is a confusion of memories for me. Some semblance of order appeared as the rescue services got things under control and I began to look forward to a couple of hours sleep before going to work. The only other recollection which is sharp in my mind is of throwing myself to the ground as an aircraft flew by at what seemed to be rooftop height. However no bombs were dropped and we all decided that the aircraft was photographing the damage caused and that it signified the end of the raid. The diagnosis seemed to be correct because before long the all-clear sounded. It began to break daylight so I went home. I later learned that nearly fifty people were killed in the bakery, including some members of the duty Home Guard.

Some days afterwards I saw my name in print for the first time. Reading the report of the platoon commander on the events of the night I saw the phrase "Volunteer S. S. Kind, although it was not his night for duty, turned out and rendered useful assistance". I felt quite proud. One should always remember Robert Burns' prayerful injunction:

Oh Lord, gie us a guid conceit o' oorsels

Chapter Four: Murphy's Law

If the German invasion of Britain had taken place what use would the Home Guard have been? What could this collection of men and boys, either too old or too young to fight in the regular forces, have done against the mighty Wermacht? Well we were in no doubt about the matter ourselves. We were convinced that we could provide that element of resistance which could be so useful to hold up an invading army until the regular forces arrived. We trained regularly and enthusiastically. Armed with elderly US army rifles our weaponry was supplemented by an array of lethal appliances of varying danger to the enemy and to ourselves. We had a Thomson sub-machine gun; this was the tommy-gun, or "Chicago Piano", of the films. We had a first world war Lewis gun and we had that utility killing instrument the Sten gun. Perhaps surprisingly we never seemed to be short of ammunition for all these and, during my two years service, I must have blazed away a significant number of cartridges.

Beyond these standard weapons we were also armed with two rather peculiar instruments of death. These were the Northover Projector and the Blacker Bombard. I suspect that these weapons were the product of an unsuccessful experimental programme which, rather than being scrapped, were handed over to the Home Guard in case they had any residual military value. The Northover Projector was a device for firing phosphorus bombs. These were tightly sealed glass bottles containing a mixture of yellow phosphorus and petrol. These hazardous objects were placed into the breech of the projector which appeared to be composed of a four foot length of metal drainpipe mounted on a tripod. The bottle was followed by a wad of something that looked like a cylinder of cotton wool, to act as a gastight plug and a protection for the bottom of the bottle, and this was followed by a charge of gun cotton. After snapping the breech shut a percussion cap was placed on a nipple on the breech and the weapon was cocked and ready for firing.

My recollection of the range is that it was about a hundred yards. It could only have been meant for firing as a mortar from a trench but we trained with it on the flat. It worked. On impact the bottles always caught fire although, at the low trajectory we used, they tended to skid leaving a long trail of flame behind them. I doubt if such a weapon would ever have been of any value for the defensive role of the Home Guard. We certainly didn't like training with it. The prospect of a glass phosphorus bomb exploding inside the barrel was rather too immediate for comfort. We never fired our other bizarre weapon, the Blacker Bombard, as far as I can remember. This remarkable weapon was a "spigot mortar" in which a finned bomb was paced on a spike or "spigot" and, on detonation, the bomb was hurled in the same sense as if a bullet stayed still whilst the gun was launched. Firing or not we went through the motions of weapon drill with it, but I doubt if it would ever have intimidated the Wermacht.

I enjoyed my two years' service in the Home Guard where, despite misdemeanour, I rose to the elevated rank of full corporal. One should not be disdainful of this modest apotheosis of my military career. I can think of at least one person, of the same rank, who was habitually called "the little corporal", even when he was in command of the entire armies of France. My command was never as large as his but sometimes I acted as guard commander with a section of beribboned old sweats from the first world war. We got on famously and, looking back, I can see that I owe a lot to these men who taught me many things, including the beginnings of that valuable adjunct to life in which I was so sadly lacking. I speak of common sense.

It was during this two years' service in the Home Guard that I first indulged in criminal activities. During one night's duty a comrade asked me if I was interested in having a cake to eat. I was. A skinny teenager, I was permanently ravenous and the prospect of something sweet and filled with cream in those days of wartime restrictions was impossible to resist. His scheme was straightforward. I kept a lookout while he picked the lock of the canteen. My effectiveness as a lookout was vitiated by my interest in the lock-picking process. This was remarkably efficient. Using an instrument made from one half of a pair of nail scissors he had the lock open within a few minutes and we helped ourselves to a delectable object known as a Chocolate Cream

Chapter Four: Murphy's Law

Swiss Roll. Carefully relocking the door we made our way back to the guard room where we enlisted the help of our comrades as accessories after the fact. This we did by dividing the stolen property equally amongst all six members of the guard. It tasted wonderful. On the basis that poachers make the best gamekeepers I've always thought that my criminal activity that night helped me towards being better at my final career job. I had learned how to pick a lock, which minor piece of knowledge joined the other mental miscellany which helped form my intellectual equipment when I became a forensic scientist.

Hopping thirty years forward it formed part of my motivation when I arranged, with a firm of safe manufacturers, that certain members of my laboratory staff who gave evidence in safe-breaking cases should learn the craft themselves. The manufacturers were quite willing to cooperate but my staff were reluctant at first because of a vague feeling that such activity might be thought unprofessional. Nevertheless I insisted and they subsequently underwent the experience of opening safes using both explosives and thermic lances. In another laboratory I insisted that some of my scientists gained the experience of throwing petrol bombs since they were currently concerned with a spate of this type of criminal activity. I encountered the same initial resistance but I think that, after the exercise, everyone agreed it had been a worthwhile exercise. Just imagine the position of an expert witness in court when counsel heaves himself to his feet and disdainfully asks "Dr Bloggs, have you ever thrown a petrol bomb?" That is surely an illustration of the rule for trial lawyers that counsel should never ask an expert witness a question unless he knows in advance what the answer is going to be.

My advocacy of such hands-on training did not meet with universal approval amongst my colleagues in the profession. I remember one of them acerbically commenting that since he was a specialist in sexual assault cases what did I suggest he did to improve his own expertise in a similar way? But it is impossible to satisfy everyone and I must return to the story of the delectable Chocolate Cream Swiss Roll. I do this because it was here that, not only did I learn to pick a lock, but I also first learned of the usefulness of transfer traces in the detection of crime.

It will be remembered that the burglary had been executed swiftly and efficiently, the scene of crime resealed, the escape made good and the spoils enjoyed amongst a group of associates. There was, however, one small blemish on the operation that prevented it being rated as a total success. This was because we had left a transferred trace of our presence at the scene of the crime, inside the locked canteen. This took the form of a large black electric lamp upon which was inscribed the quite unequivocal identification "Home Guard". I will omit the sequel, which was rather an uncomfortable one, except to say that the platoon commander said he was quite sure that I was the worst liar he had ever met. I still occasionally re-analyse the semantic implications of this statement. This example of plain human ineptitude (forget the moral aspects for the moment) is but one minuscule example of the part that stupidity consistently plays in human affairs, but it was the first time the fact had been brought home to me. There will be other, more sombre, examples later in this book but whilst I am in a confessional mood let me tell you of two other, comparatively trivial, illustrations of the general theme. The first requires us to go forward two years in time from the case of the Chocolate cream Swiss Roll.

In my first year in the Royal Air Force, in 1943, I had to sit an examination in elementary air navigation. Together with about twenty other air cadets I was presented with a question paper of basic mathematics, geometry and simple navigational problems. Each of us had to pass this examination in order to proceed to more advanced problems along the track towards becoming fully fledged air navigators.

It was a beautiful summer's day and I remember the sun streaming through the windows of the examination room and the flight-lieutenant instructor sitting as invigilator on the podium. The subject of navigation fascinated me and I was quite confident I would get a good mark. Around me my comrades were working feverishly and the place was totally silent except for the sound of heavy breathing and the occasional rustle of paper. I worked systematically through the question paper with great concentration and when I had completed the questions, with an abundance of time to spare, I carefully went through them again and checked the answers. They were all correct. None of my companions appeared to have finished the paper but there seemed little point in hanging about and, with half an hour to spare, I handed in my answer papers to the flight lieutenant instructor and left the examination room. It is best to draw a veil over what transpired between then and the examination review session some days later, except to say that I entered the session with enhanced knowledge and a feeling of dread. The post mortem took place in the original examination room, with the same instructor sitting at the same desk on the same podium. I recollect he was a most courteous and kindly man with a Yorkshire accent and an obvious determination to do the best he could for his cadets. In civil life he had been a schoolteacher and he still retained some of the mannerisms of his profession. He shuffled the papers before him, arranged them in neat piles on the desk, and then called for silence. "Good morning gentlemen" he said. "Before I start the session I have an apology to make to one of you. Cadet Kind, I am sorry, it appears that I have lost some of your answer papers". I jumped to attention and replied "No Sir, you have not, I forgot to turn the question paper over".

The gale of laughter quickly died as the instructor's face darkened and it was in total silence that he said. "Cadet Kind, that possibility had occurred to me but I dismissed it from my mind because I decided, after long reflection, that no-one could conceivably be that stupid". He was wrong. I was doubly stupid of course. Firstly for making the mistake and secondly for not taking the opportunity he offered me to avoid the ridicule of my comrades. Since that incident, over half a century ago, I've often wondered whether the instructor deliberately worded his announcement to provide me with the chance of escape from the consequences of my own folly. With the passage of the years I have come to believe that he did. He was a very shrewd and penetrating man and his mind, I am now sure, worked in dimensions unknown to mentally feverish young men whose major ambition was to experience the excitement of war. So, if the spirit of my instructor still inhabits some timeless, omnipercipient, corner of the cosmos, I wish to apologise.

I am very sorry Sir. You are a gentleman and I am most grateful for the efforts that you made on my behalf. I am a fool.

The last example of a stupid error which had conspicuous consequences concerned my involvement in the design of a new forensic science laboratory in the 1970s. I came into the design process rather late. In fact the foundations of the laboratory had already been laid so I visited the site to see what was irrevocable and what might be changed should it be necessary. On seeing the site I formed the view that major errors of design had been made which, were they not immediately rectified, would require comparatively expensive correction later. I was contemptuous that such elementary errors should have been passed by the architect employed by the organisation in which I worked. I said as much, both at length and colourfully, in a letter to my chief in London. Next, having worked off my head of steam, I wrote a reasoned and restrained letter on the same subject to the architect himself. The discerning reader of these words will have already have noted the development of a hazardous situation, but nothing was further from my preoccupied mind than the possibility of the elementary error which in fact occurred. My efficient secretary, being away at the time, the despatch of the letters was undertaken by an office junior. She placed the letter to each individual in the envelope addressed to the other. I fulminated for long afterwards about the "stupid office girl" but later it came home to me that the fact of the matter was that the substantive fault, yet again, was my own. Persons in senior positions are paid to take the responsibility to ensure that such situations do not arise. Murphy's Law states:

If it is possible for something to go wrong then, sooner or later, it will.

and it is the duty of the senior manager to frustrate Murphy at every turn, a duty I signally failed to discharge.

Chapter Four: Murphy's Law

During the war I left my job as errand boy at the Nottingham Co-op when an opportunity arose to be a laboratory assistant in the pharmacy department at University College Nottingham. Nevertheless I stayed with the Co-op platoon of the Home Guard. At UCN I worked in the main building, a white limestone pile immortalised by D H Lawrence as being in a "grand and cakey style". Many of the staff were away fighting and this included the laboratory steward who would have been my immediate boss. His wartime substitute was a woman, a junior academic, a rather pretty lady who blushed easily. I think she found it intimidating having a pair of pubescent teenage boys (I had a colleague) as assistants.

Our duties were not onerous. The refilling of reagent bottles and the polishing of laboratory benches were the major ones and these, with a modicum of application, only took up part of our time. Thereafter, to fill time we got up to many pranks, some of them quite dangerous. We absorbed a lot of crude chemistry during the course of the day and supplemented this at the night school which we were compelled to attend as a condition of the job. As a consequence of this we were always experimenting when authority's back was turned. The other laboratory assistant was a boy of adventurous spirit, unlimited imagination and steely nerves. Looking back it seems that far too many of my associates in early life possessed these hazardous attributes. I shall draw a discreet veil over our unauthorised and perilous experiments with the exception of one which I only mention because it contains a useful practical lesson for any forensic scientist

One of the substances used in pharmacy is called "pyroxylin" and it is used, in dissolved form, to form an artificial skin over minor injuries. It is a close relative of gun-cotton and it possesses some of gun-cotton's qualities. One of these is that if you place some pyroxylin in an open vessel and ignite it, it will burn away swiftly and silently. On the other hand if you place it in a restricted space and ignite it, it will explode with a violence proportional to the degree of restriction. One day my fellow laboratory assistant called me into the dispensary to demonstrate an unofficial experiment he had set up with pyroxylin. This experiment I will describe to you in a moment but first let me tell you about the dispensary itself.

This was an impressive place with something of the dignity of a well-kept library in the stately home of a duke, but with bottles in place of the books. There was a large polished mahogany rostrum upon which figures of authority sat from time to time, and this was surrounded by a series of working benches for the students, similarly made of polished mahogany. The waxed wooden parquet flooring glistened discreetly and all the walls were lined with crystal clear glass shelves. The shelves themselves were open, with the exception of those bearing the poisons bottles, which were behind locked glass cupboard doors. The bottles of drugs were legion and wonderful, and what labels! Recessed into the glass of the bottles they were ceramic masterpieces and their legends were in black letters on a white background surrounded by chestnut coloured and gold leaf frames. "*Liq. sod. chlor. chir.*" indicated a surgical solution of chlorinated soda. "*Mist. kaolin*" indicated kaolin mixture and even distilled water was indicated with panache as "*Aqua destillata*". "*Oleum junip*" contained the oil of juniper which the boss used each morning as part of his hair-of-the-dog antidote to the previous night's imbibitions.

The boss himself, head of the department and a pharmacist of high distinction, was larger than life. Physically big he was permanently in army uniform with the rank emblems of a major and sporting Royal Flying Corps wings above the rows of medal ribbons on his breast. He was the commanding officer of the University College Officer Training Corps. He had a well developed sense of priorities and we seldom saw him in the department except when he was giving his lectures or mixing his early morning potions. He had his own small part of the war to run. I always acted as projectionist at his lectures and I absorbed from them much that was useful in later life. Naturally somewhat acerbic he was basically a kindly man and he would sometimes come into the departmental stores where we laboratory boys had our headquarters. There he would expound at length on how to fly a first world-war fighter plane. Even now I can hear his voice describing the hair raising procedure of landing a Sopwith Camel. I think the enjoyment of listening to him was one of the reasons that I decided to join the Royal Air Force and to be a pilot. However, had I stuck to this ambition I doubt if I would have seen any action during the war but for the moment I shall return to the dispensary and to my perilous colleague.

There in the middle of a bench stood the experiment ready to be performed. It consisted of an empty metal-polish tin out of the top of which protruded a short piece of string. The significance of the design escaped me for the moment so he proceeded to enlighten me. The tin, he informed me, was full of pyroxylin and the string was impregnated with potassium nitrate which made it an excellent slow-burning fuse. He now proposed to light the fuse he said and, good as his word, he picked up a lighted bunsen burner and did so. I was horrified and began to back away towards the door.

My companion laughed at my concern. It was pure bravado on his part and he had no intention of allowing the fuse to burn its full length. After a short time he reached out to remove the glowing thread but he had left it rather late and had difficulty grasping hold of it. Leaving him to make the best he could of the situation I turned and ran. I must have been a good twenty yards down the corridor when there was an enormous explosion. I stopped, turned and ran back expecting to see my colleague badly injured but he was still standing there, now looking slightly bewildered, and on the bench in front of him was the metal polish tin, now somewhat changed in appearance. The top was still there and the base was still there but, in between, the entire cylinder had been stripped into ribbons which remained attached to the vertical soldered seam of the tin. This object was now resting on a surface of white unburnt pyroxylin and the whole looked something like a bizarre snow-covered Christmas nativity scene.

I heard shouts in the distance and once again I decided that my companion had best deal with the matter himself. I quickly went into the stores and started to wash glassware with as innocent and unconcerned an appearance as my fast-beating heart would allow. After a time one of the lecturers came into the stores. "What the devil was that explosion Kind?" he said. My answer was the best I could do at the time. "I think it was a car backfiring in the service entrance, sir" I replied. His face was a dark mask of suspicion as he looked at me but he said no more and, after a moment, he went out of the stores. I could hear him walking about and searching for some time but finally his footsteps receded down the corridor and silence reigned once more. It seemed to me that the most fitting thing I could do under the circumstances was to continue washing up and let things take their own course and this I did. However, after half an hour or so, I finally went to the dispensary to investigate. My companion was nowhere to be seen and neither was the metal polish tin. A few specks of pyroxylin lay scattered here and there but apart from this the dispensary was a scene of tranquillity and there was no hint of damage anywhere.

It was the following morning before I saw the hapless experimenter again. He had sticking plaster across his forehead but was otherwise uninjured and he soon told me what had happened the previous day after my speedy exit from the dispensary. In attempting to remove the burning fuse from the tin he had inadvertently knocked it further in and, when he saw that an explosion was inevitable, he ducked. He was almost below the level of the bench top when the explosion occurred and the blast caught him across the upper part of his forehead. After he had picked himself up, and regained his wits, he heard the staff member run down the corridor and into the stores. Subsequently the suspicious lecturer had even come into the dispensary but he had stayed by the door and saw neither the residue of the explosion, nor the miscreant who kept well below bench top level. Had the pyroxylin all exploded there is little doubt that he would have been killed but, as the pressure built up from the burning chemical, the flimsy tin had ruptured and the greater part of the explosive was scattered unburnt. Later in life I was to learn that a similar process tends to occur when criminals fire sawn-off shotguns. Shot gun cartridge propellants are designed to burn at such a rate that the pressure is progressively built up as the charge of shot proceeds up the barrel. With most of the barrel missing much of the charge remains unburnt. The principle is similar in both cases.

My service as a laboratory assistant at UCN terminated when I decided that the pittance which the college paid me was unworthy of my services. In truth the college intended the job to be a stepping stone to higher academic things and the low pay was more than compensated by the learning facilities afforded us. However this argument escaped me at the time and I was only conscious of the fact that my contemporaries always had much more money than I did. I left and took a job as a heavy lorry driver. This really was a remarkable achievement because I couldn't drive. Nevertheless by convincing the haulage firm owner that I was a quick learner I got myself a job at the age of seventeen at the princely sum of five pounds a week. This was ten times what I had received as a laboratory assistant. "Heavy lorry" did I say? Well not exactly because it was meant to carry only a one-and-a-half-ton load . However by the time the boss had built up the sides with wooden planks, and substituted the single back wheels with heavy duty twin wheels, it was capable of carrying five tons of sugar beet. This load I regularly carried, three times a day, throughout the autumn of 1942.

Together with my "mate", a boy of fifteen who was a much better driver than I (but an illegal one), we made our three trips per day from the sugar beet fields to the factory where we tipped our load into large silos. The vehicle was weighed once going in full, and again when coming out empty, and the difference was taken as the weight of the delivered sugar beet. There was, however, a correction to make for the amount of mud sticking to the beet and this was done by a factory employee selecting about a dozen "representative" beet from the load on entry, just after the weighbridge. This meant of course that we always loaded the dirty beet first and the clean beet later and the moral aspects of such a practice never concerned me. Everyone knew that the custom was a general one and I've no doubt that an adjustment was made for this. One might call it the "notional mud correction factor" but such semantic considerations were far from my mind in those days.

The Sceptical Witness

The biggest problem was loading the stuff and this we did with enormous hand forks, the tines of which were terminated by spherical metal balls to prevent the beet being speared and so having to be pulled off individually by hand. We loaded fifteen tons per day on average between the two of us and I've no doubt it did us a world of good. On the other hand I doubt if it did our little truck any good, converting it to something of a lethal weapon. Although the rear wheels had been changed to compensate for the gross overloading, the rest of the system, including the transmission, brakes and springs, was that of a light lorry. Looking back I shudder at my memories of going down hill, in first gear, with both the hand brake and footbrake hard on and the engine screaming in front of us, and five tons of sugar beet just behind us ready to make a sort of sugar beet mousse of us should we have hit anything. But we survived and I kept the job for several months until I finally gave it up because of the necessity to leave home at 5am and not arrive back until after 7pm by which time I was so tired I could only just eat and go to bed. I missed the company of my friends. My parents were very relieved when I gave the job up, not withstanding the substantial loss of income to the family's modest budget. Five pounds a week was a lot to lose for a working class family in those days.

So towards the end of 1942 I found myself jobless and approaching my eighteenth birthday. I had already volunteered for aircrew in the Royal Air Force for which the minimum entry age was eighteen. Thus my position was such that I would be nominally eligible for entry a few weeks after leaving my job. There was a snag however. Aircrew service was a popular option for young men and, even after the age of eighteen, there was a waiting period of several months before call-up. So, with my eldest brother in North Africa with the Eighth Army, and my middle brother training in Scotland as a wireless operator/air gunner, I put my mind to finding a method of circumventing the system and getting in on the action myself. This I did by writing to the authorities and pleading that I found it impossible to get a job, because prospective employers were not interested when they found out I was liable to be called up in the near future. This was simply a lie, almost

Chapter Four: Murphy's Law

anyone could get a job in those days but the lie worked and, as a "compassionate case", I was called up ahead of my time . The "compassionate case" label had an interesting consequence which I shall describe later.

The Sceptical Witness

Chapter Five: Man Is Not Lost

And so it happened that at the beginning of February 1943, a few days after my eighteenth birthday, I travelled to the Aircrew Receiving Centre in London. Commonly known as "ACRC" (and by several disrespectful variants) the "centre" was a rather diffuse organisation which was distributed around several widely spaced locations. The sleeping quarters comprised several blocks of luxury flats in St. John's Wood, the canteen was located in the Zoological Gardens in Regents Park, and the classrooms were widely scattered at a variety of places ranging from London University to Lords Cricket Ground. Sick bay was in one of the local hospitals, but which one I forget.

I have a good reason for forgetting. Only a day or two after my arrival at ACRC I went down with a very bad attack of what was said to be influenza and I was taken to sick bay. The interview with the medical officer, which led to my dispatch to sick bay, remains in my memory as a most unpleasant and hallucinatory experience. The MO was a young and freshly qualified medic. Wearing the virgin rank markings of a newly appointed Flight Lieutenant, and a terminally bored expression, he sat at his desk dispensing his own version of succour to the afflicted. At the time of my interview I was suffering from the impression that I was floating somewhere in outer space. I stood swaying and very ill before the MO's desk, restrained from falling only by the sympathetic hand of a medical orderly. There was no examination or other investigation of my condition. I think the MO must have diagnosed my affliction as I came through the door. So "influenza" it was. A necessary demonstration of expertise in many fields, as I was to learn later in my career, was to "give it a name".

You want to go to sick bay I suppose?" snarled the MO as a comradely ending to our short acquaintance. I tried to form a comprehensible reply but the words did not seem to form as they usually did and, after a moment listening to my incoherent noises, he growled at the orderly "take him away" and off I went, half staggering and half carried. I was very ill but, with whatever reasoning power that remained in my throbbing head, I formulated an implacable distaste for the MO and a determination to deal with him after the war. But, apart from some slight relief to my feelings, my intentions were quite useless because I was incapable of taking the basic precautions of remembering the MO's name and appearance. "Making a note at the time" did not become an essential part of my life until almost ten years later. Perhaps in a future existence some celestial and omnipotent appeal court judge will extend to me the privilege of reviewing the MO's case before I despatch his eternal spirit over the edge into a cauldron of everlasting hellfire and abiding cosmic influenza.

The trouble with the MO, I think, was that he was thoroughly bored with a job that limited him, irrevocably, to his professional functions at desk or bedside, whereas all his patients were men of about his own age who were headed for the excitement of war. Military aircraft do not carry doctors. He'd have been happier in the navy. All this can be said in excuse for him and there may be other unexpectedly telling points in his favour. I only knew him for a couple of hazy minutes, so perhaps I am being unfair and I would not wish to be that. Since that interview I have so often been impressed by a powerful case for the prosecution, only to be subsequently disenchanted by an even better one for the defence, that it has made me a very much more cautious man. I am now fully aware of the dangers of making up my mind in the absence of all the evidence. So, at that distant location in space and time, when I hope to meet the MO on equal terms, with me (and doubtless him) morally strengthened by a half century of life's slings and arrows, I have resolved to listen quietly and patiently to everything he has to say for himself. Then he's for the bottomless pit.

I was several days in sick bay but I remember nothing of them and, when I finally regained a reasonable body temperature and some degree of lucidity I returned to my billet to rejoin my intake. Whatever I missed whilst I was in hospital didn't seem to matter much because I was not put back into a later intake to start again.

We were instructed how to fold our blankets and to arrange our equipment on the bed for inspection. We were shown how to "blanco" our webbing belts to a most dazzling white and to clean our brass buttons

Chapter Five: Man Is Not Lost

to a golden mirror finish. We were taught to stand rigidly to attention when the inspecting officer made his rounds each morning. We were made to form up on parade at specified hours of the day, each of us proudly wearing the white cap flash of an aircrew cadet, to be marched off to our various duties. These ranged from doing parade ground drill, undergoing medical examinations, listening to lectures on discipline and completing an interminable series of printed forms. For many of us it was our first absence from home and we were precipitated from a world which was an extension of our childhood into a community where self reliance was a major necessity for a tolerable life. Note I do not say "the major necessity" because the armed services themselves provide a wrap-around safety net in the form of bed, board, clothing and a modest pay packet. Nevertheless within these bulwarks each had to cultivate a habit of looking after himself faced by all those problems which, at home, had often been solved by parents and elder siblings.

We quickly and easily formed friendships, most of which were destined to dissolve as the requirements of war posted individuals according to the "exigencies of the service" and the whims of the clerks in the records office. Come to think of it, I'm not sure that I've ever heard the word "exigency" used in spoken English since my war-time service. In the manner of brash young men we boasted of how we were perfectly capable of flouting authority and getting away with it, and we cultivated a devil-may-care attitude to what the sergeant said to us, always making sure first that he was not within earshot. As in all such groups there were a few conformists, young men who were old and responsible beyond their years, and whose efficiency and sobriety was a constant and irritating reminder to us, the rash majority, of how we should behave.

There was one of these admirable characters in our own barrack room. A quiet, courteous and studious individual, he was always in bed at a reasonable hour, he never went out drinking with his comrades and he was always up first in the morning. Each morning his equipment was immaculately ready for inspection before he went off for the half mile early morning walk to the Zoological Gardens canteen, to be first in the queue for breakfast. On one occasion we played a mean trick on him and, even now, I squirm when I think of it. It happened like this.

One night all the occupants of our barrack room, with his exception, went out drinking together. We returned just before the deadline of 11pm and made our way to where our comrade, the sole occupant of the barrack room, was already soberly asleep. His equipment was neatly stacked ready for formal inspection on the following morning. On a chair by the side of his bed lay his wrist watch and it was this which inserted the germ of a malicious idea into our minds. Miserable creatures that we were, we changed the time on his wrist watch from 11pm to 7am, then we readjusted our own watches to the same time. Next we undressed and, at a signal, started to dress again while one of our number shook our sleeping comrade into wakefulness and told him, in an urgent tone, that it was 7am and time that he got out of bed. The victim looked about him in disbelief as he saw his room mates busy dressing and he promptly consulted his watch. To help him to confirm that the time he saw there was correct, each of us benevolently displayed his own watch to the victim. Bearing in mind that on a February day in the latitude of London it is just as dark at 7am as it is at 11pm, there was absolutely no way the victim could tell that he was being fooled, other than by the disparate signals being given to him by his own body clock.

"Oh God" he moaned "I feel as if I've only been in bed for half an hour". This nearly ruined the whole scheme, being absolutely true, and the stifled peals of laughter were instantly transformed into an enormous bout of communal coughing. Dragging himself out of bed the victim went through his usual sequence of washing, shaving (he obviously noticed nothing amiss there) and then he dressed. Finally he arranged all his gear into inspection order on his bed, put on his greatcoat, picked up his mess tin, and went out into the freezing night. Throughout all this sequence his roommates had been "dressing" at a decreasing rate and consequently it was a half clothed band which covertly followed him out on to the parade ground to witness his progress towards the main gate. One section of the gate was still open, doubtless for the use of those of sufficiently exalted rank not to be subject to the restrictions which were applied to mere cadets. It was towards this outlet that our luckless victim made his way. He never passed through it.

"Airman!" cried a foghorn voice deeply modulated with tones of menace, "where the 'ell you think you're going?"
"I'm going to breakfast, corporal" was our room-mate's reply to the service policeman who was now emerging from the gatehouse.
"What, at bleedin' midnight?" said the corporal, "You tryin' to be bleedin' funny?"

Although phonetically distorted and lexically restricted, it became evident that the corporal's message was getting through and, after a period of rather quieter conversational exchange, our roommate turned and walked, very slowly and dispiritedly, back to the main barracks door. We all turned and fled back to our room and, when the victim entered, we were all "asleep" in our beds. He said nothing but simply busied himself rearranging his gear, re-making his bed and undressing. With his pyjamas on he looked around him, saw that all the beds were occupied, walked over to the switch and put the light out before climbing into his bed. "Last man into bed puts the light out" was the rule and, being a responsible individual, he dutifully followed it. Already the suspicion was awakening in my mind that we were a group of miserable creatures to play such an underhand trick and by next morning my suspicion had hardened to a conviction. Nothing more was ever said about the matter by any one of us. Embarrassment on one side and shame on the other was probably the reason. Which side was which? I'm not sure.

Of the various friends I made in my first few weeks of service one stands out very clearly in my mind. In his middle twenties he presented a sophisticated personality and a knowledgeable outlook which stirred and impressed my provincial mind. His name was Max and he was a native of a small paradise in the Indian Ocean, the island of

Mauritius. Of predominantly French language and culture Mauritius had been annexed by the British in 1814 and, twenty years later, the African slaves had been emancipated. This was followed by a large immigration of Indian labourers. Why do I bother to recount this chapter of European imperial history? Simply because Max was its outcome. The rich blood which flowed in his veins was a mixture of European colonists, African slaves and Indian immigrants and it had been matured by over a century of Mauritian sun. He was both a gentleman and a gentle man.

The age difference between my eighteen and his twenty five years was quite a wide one too from my adolescent standpoint. He was a cultivated man and fully bilingual in English and French, a fact which impressed my half educated mind most profoundly. He regularly quoted, and sometimes wrote, poetry and he spent much of his modest pay on eating out on dishes more to his taste than the canteen food served to us new recruits. One evening I plucked up courage and asked if I could go out with him to dinner and he readily agreed. The courage-plucking on my part was necessary because I had never been to a restaurant before and the name of the establishment Max frequented sounded impossibly high class. Nevertheless I was resigned to spending most of my week's pay on a single meal at "Leon's". But even with the decision made to spend so much money I still felt a profound relief when we arrived at our destination and it turned out to be Lyon's Corner House, a popular and cheap establishment much used by office workers. Evidently the French half of Max's linguistic equipment had taken control at a critical moment.

His choice of dish matched his mixed African, European and Indian blood; it was a curry. "I'll have the same" I said. Max was rather concerned at this choice and I had to admit to him, under questioning, that I hadn't the faintest idea what curry was. He suggested something milder but I stuck to my choice, the evening was an adventure and I was not going to sully it with steak and kidney pudding or the like. The curry was fiercely pimented and it brought hot and stinging tears to my eyes. Nevertheless I struggled through it to the end under Max's watchful and concerned gaze, stubbornly insisting that I was enjoying every mouthful. The following week we returned to Lyon's and once again I ordered curry. I was unwilling to lose face and admit that, on the previous occasion, I had found the taste verging on the lethal. But strangely, this time I found the curry quite palatable. Perhaps it was a case of adaptation, or else the first searing dish had killed off my more sensitive taste buds.

Throughout all the years since my visits to Lyon's with Max, curry has been one of my favourite dishes. I have bored friends and colleagues *ad nauseam* by boasting how, on recounting the tale of my curry initiation to the Government Chemist of another Indian Ocean paradise island, he immediately had a large batch made up for me personally. This was of his wife's own special recipe. Few curry addicts can boast a supply of curry powder personally certified by a Government Chemist. But this was many years after the war.

Max and I compendiously discussed life, fate, the world, the weather and the human race, as together we ate curried dishes at Lyon's Corner House in London. But after a few weeks our paths diverged and we were posted to different stations. I never heard of him again until forty years later when in 1983, a senior forensic pathologist from Mauritius visited my laboratory. I told him about my wartime friend and it proved that, when my visitor was a child at primary school, Max had been his teacher. Through this coincidence Max and I got in touch again and for several years we corresponded and reminisced as old men do, planning all the while to meet again as soon as possible. Then it became too late. The road to hell is paved with good intentions but that was not the road my good and kindly friend took when he died, I am quite sure of that. He was an admirable and gentle man and I really should have kept in mind that, for each one of us, the number of tomorrows lessens inexorably every day.

From St. John's Wood and the administrative maelstrom of the Aircrew Receiving Centre I was then posted to RAF Hornchurch, in Essex, a fighter station of Battle of Britain fame. This was quite remarkable because I went there for my Initial Training Wing course. An Initial Training Wing was an organisation where budding aircrew underwent instruction and assessment before the successful ones went on to further training in specialist aircrew categories elsewhere. Most ITWs were large organisations which were specifically dedicated to this type of elementary training and it was surprising to find one, albeit small, on an operational Spitfire fighter station. There was a further peculiarity in that the preponderance of air cadets at Hornchurch ITW were overseas personnel, mainly Irish Free State citizens and Latin Americans, together with a sprinkling of American, French and Malayan nationals. My recollection is that I was one of only two Englishmen on my own course but it didn't occur to me to question the national mix until later in my training. This was prompted because it transpired that no-one of my subsequent comrades had ever heard of Hornchurch ITW. The fighter station yes, the ITW no. It was obviously some sort of special unit for overseas people but this raised the question why I, an Englishman, had been sent there.

The most plausible explanation was made to me, much later, by someone at my last RAF station, at Folkingham in Lincolnshire. It was after the end of the war, in 1946, when service personnel were being kept busy to allow a gradual release of labour on to the post-war market rather than in one sudden flood. The station records clerk, a corporal, had been whiling away his time as he awaited release by reading the personal records of all the servicemen on the station. When he came to my record he was intrigued by the fact that I had entered aircrew training ahead of my turn. Since there was no longer any need to keep my misdemeanour quiet I told him that I had lied in 1942 and I had been taken in as a "compassionate case" ahead of my time. At that moment it occurred to me that this was the reason that I had been shunted away from the main training stream to the minor Hornchurch Initial Training Wing. In a normal ITW my age would have been noticed and I would have been seen as "jumping the queue" with a possible implied criticism of the fairness of the system. Seniority was jealously guarded by potential aircrew trainees. Any apparent favouritism by the selectors had to be rigidly concealed.

Chapter Five: Man Is Not Lost

But, for whatever reason, in 1943 I was there at Hornchurch for a very busy and enjoyable year. Our living quarters were in a former hospital, "Suttons", on the far side of the airfield from the hangars, flying control and the other operational buildings. As a virtually self-contained unit we were little involved with the daily life of the Spitfire squadrons based there, but we had certain minimal duties in common with all the other station personnel. One of these was to learn to operate the machine gun clusters which were located in a series of dugouts around the airfield perimeter track. These killing weapons were beautifully engineered, as so many weapons of death are, and they were mounted in precisely balanced clusters which allowed them to be manually traversed through 360 degrees and fired by a single gunner. The guns were permanently armed with belts of ammunition and they required only the pull of a single cocking lever for them to be ready for firing. We cadets had to learn how to use them because it was required, should the station be attacked by low flying enemy aircraft, that the nearest personnel took over the guns and operated them. There was no question of permanent manning for what was a fairly improbable event. The first man there got the job.

I used to dream about manning the guns under fire in a "Boys Own Paper" manner and, whenever I walked by the emplacements, I found my pace slowing and my eyes scanning the horizon, willing a low level attack by enemy aircraft and my personal moment of ballistic glory. But the moment never came. It was a good thing that we had regular lessons in aircraft recognition and that I was fully capable of distinguishing a Supermarine Spitfire from a Messerschmitt 109. Later in life it became apparent to me that the more determined people are, and determination can border upon desperation, the less critical they become and the more they tend to see what they want to see. The police investigator who has laboured long and unsuccessfully in a particular case may adopt, as a main suspect, someone who would hardly merit such concentrated attention in less desperate circumstances. The mother despairingly searching for a lost child may uncritically run to examine a child spotted in the distance whereas in less harrowing circumstances she would be immediately aware that it was not her own.

The Sceptical Witness

None of this is a plea for indecision but I've occasionally wondered since that time what nightmare scenario might have led me to shoot down a Spitfire which was innocently "beating up" the station, under the impression that it was an Me 109.

But even in the absence of airfield attack we did have other moments of excitement. When darkness fell we could watch the bombing raids on London, ten miles to the West. From a safe distance we could see the flash of the bombs as they struck, and the bursts of anti-aircraft shells rather like tiny sparkling fireworks in the sky. Sometimes we witnessed the launch of a large group of anti aircraft rockets but these seemed always to detonate too low down, in a veritable raft of explosions, at about half the height of the shell bursts. At a distance of ten miles there was no question of matching flash and explosion, and all we heard was an occasional dull rumble as the sounds of war were blunted by distance.

On one sunny day I witnessed the remarkable sight of a United States Air Force B17 Flying Fortress bomber land at Hornchurch. This was surprising because the airfield was a only a relatively small grass field which was not adapted for enormous four engined heavy bombers. Furthermore the front half of the bomber's tail fin was missing, shot off by anti aircraft fire over Germany. As I watched it the silver giant came down to a perfect three-point touchdown, about two hundred yards from where I was standing, and then it slowed quickly on the tiny patch of grassland as the pilot applied maximum brakes. At the far end of the field, now down to a walking pace, the Fortress turned and taxied over to Flying Control where the pilot neatly parked it adjacent to some Spitfires and then cut the engines. It was a masterly performance by the pilot and I imagined his crew cheering him to the echo as he found their salvation in a small green field in Essex.

It was off-duty time for the air cadets and I ran indoors to tell my comrades of the unexpected arrival. They were playing cards and their first reaction was that either my aircraft recognition was faulty or I was hallucinating. Nevertheless I sped over to the apron in front of

Chapter Five: Man Is Not Lost

Flying Control and there it was, an enormous silver metal bird, dominating the adjacent Spitfires as a bald eagle might tower over a group of sparrowhawks. The only damage to the bomber seemed confined to the tail fin, but here much of the internal structure of the fin was exposed. I looked and marvelled at the solidly engineered structure which had allowed the pilot to fly his crippled machine back from Germany, then over France and the English Channel, without the fin being torn away by the rush of the slipstream, until he was able to put down at the first available airfield.

I made many friends at Hornchurch, including an American who had come over some time previously, before the entry of the USA into the war, to join the Royal Air Force. We used to play poker together but he, although enthusiastic, was not a very good player. One pay day I won all his pay but, to enable him to go out for the evening, I generously lent him ten shillings of it back. We both went out to the local dance hall where we met two girls. I'm still married to one and so he was to the other until his death robbed a happily married couple of their golden wedding anniversary a few years ago. Philosophers divide happenings into those of chance and those of necessity. The sad part of my stay at Hornchurch was the news of the death of my middle brother, Alan. At 5am on the 11th of August, 1943 his Halifax aircraft, travelling on a northerly course, was approaching Selsey Bill on the South coast of England, returning after a bombing raid on Nuremberg. The aircraft had been airborne for seven and a half hours, fuel was running low and visibility was poor. The wireless operator, my brother, had been trying for an hour to obtain a bearing which would guide his aircraft to the nearest airfield, but he had had no success.

The fuel situation became critical as the Halifax crossed the coast and the captain gave the order to abandon the aircraft. All seven crew members, including the captain himself, baled out successfully. Unfortunately a strong off-shore wind was blowing and all except the captain of the aircraft, the pilot, were blown out to sea. Four hours later the navigator was picked up, cold and exhausted, by an air sea rescue launch.

The Sceptical Witness

Over the ensuing several weeks the bodies of four of the remaining five crew members were picked up but the wireless operator, my brother, was never found. His unmarked grave is in the English Channel. His memorial is his name, amongst thousands of other British and Commonwealth aircrew, on the Royal Air Force Runnymede Memorial near London. Runnymede, where the *Magna Carta* was signed. The "Great Charter", the first written and detailed statement of English Law, agreed in 1215 between a tyrant king and his barons, and still an influence today upon the life and laws of all English speaking countries. Perhaps the ghosts of King John and Sergeant Alan William Kind sometimes speak together

...among the reeds at Runnymede.

It was the incident of my brother's death which caused me to change my intention from being a pilot to that of being a navigator. Probably quite unfairly I concluded that my brother's death was the consequence of navigational errors and I decided that I might, in some way, redress his death by becoming a competent guide to my crew. This decision accelerated my progress towards operational flying because it cut out several months of Elementary Flying Training School.

So my next station was an air navigation school on the Isle of Man. This distinctive little island lies centrally in the Irish Sea midway between England, Ireland, Scotland and Wales. Mountainous for the most part, it has a small northern plain where there was located Royal Air Force Station, Jurby. Steeped in Celtic and Viking history, the island's Tynwald Court and its House of Keys comprise one of the most ancient legislative assemblies in the world. Not that we young men were very conscious of the layers of history beneath our feet. In 1944 we were much too busy learning to navigate military aircraft and, when we were not doing that, enjoying ourselves. It was an ideal place to learn air navigation because for much of the time we flew in sight of some distinctively shaped coast or island which established our position and allowed us to navigate our way safely back to base.

Chapter Five: Man Is Not Lost

But simple map reading was not sufficient and, after the early stages of training, the student navigator had to produce evidence, in the navigator's flight log, that bearings on lighthouses or other geographical points, and sextant sights upon stars, had been used. I still have my Royal Air Force astronomical "Sight Log Book". On the front cover is the reproduction of a mediaeval woodcut which shows a navigator using a crude precursor to the sextant. Beneath this is the caption "Man is Not Lost". This may have been the precursor of yet another motto common during my training. "A good navigator is never lost. He may be uncertain of his position but he is never lost". Usually recited to the accompaniment of guffaws of laughter there is nevertheless a kernel of truth in the quotation. It is better to act on uncertain and limited information than on none at all.

But whatever the technique used, the problem was always the same. To set off from base, to fly a prearranged route under certain specified conditions, and to arrive back successfully without running out of fuel, or flying into the top of a mountain that you hadn't noticed was there. Unhappily this last event was not uncommon among passing military aircraft. The problem was that over the Irish Sea there passed a busy air route between England and Northern Ireland. Pilots unaccustomed to flying this route sometimes paid too little regard to the presence of Snaefell mountain reaching up out of the wide flat plain of the Irish Sea. In low cloud some didn't see it before it was too late. Others didn't see it at all. The results were equally fatal. I remember walking on Snaefell in the summer of 1944 among the newly arrived wreckage of a Liberator bomber when a piece of white silk parachute attracted me. I picked it up and then quickly put it down again when I saw what lay underneath. As far as I know these misfortunes never happened to Jurby aircrews, we were too conscious of the looming presence of Snaefell on the approach to the airfield. Unless he was certain of the aircraft's position, a pilot never flew below the height of the nearest mountain, plus a few hundred feet to spare. It was the duty of the navigator to reassure him on the matter. When I die I think that the figure 2034 will be found engraved upon my heart. That is the height in feet of Snaefell, the "snow mountain" of the Vikings.

The Sceptical Witness

So I spent most of 1944 on the Isle of Man, studying air navigation and, unknown to me at the time, acquiring an attitude of mind which was to colour my approach to scientific research and crime investigation in the years to come. But what does an air navigator do which could possibly condition his attitudes to investigation? On the face of it scientific research and crime investigation appear to be subjects quite isolated from air navigation. The routine task of the air navigator is to work out the direction and speed his aircraft is travelling over the ground. This he does from a knowledge of how fast, and in what direction, the aircraft is travelling through the air and then, by combining this with the direction and speed of the wind, he obtains a resultant "track" over the ground and his ground speed. From this he can tell the pilot what the aircraft position is at any given time, what is the required course to steer to any required destination and the estimated time of arrival (ETA) there. He also learns a miscellany of other techniques such as whether, at any given moment in flight, it is quicker to return to base or to continue on to the destination. This sort of information can be of value when something goes wrong.

The air navigator knows the power of numerical and graphical methods in the solution of practical problems but he is not entirely limited by his calculations. He is a master of approximation in assessing the scale of a problem. He is not disturbed if his preconceived flight plan proves to be in error. It usually is to some degree because it is based upon predictions and predictions are often wrong. He simply sets about modifying his flight plan according to the new information available. Air navigation is not a static undertaking, conditions are always changing and the navigator's practice is one of continual adjustment and reiterative fine tuning as the situation develops. Using modern computer jargon, he works in a real-time world. In this world of the air navigator, as in the worlds of the research scientist and the crime investigator, fact must modify theory, not vice versa. Any mental model or theory must be recognised as subordinate to the facts. For the navigator a positively established "fix" must supplant any calculated position, no matter how elegantly established. A navigator becomes instinctively aware of the interplay of time, distance, direction, position, season, hours of darkness and the practical constraints these factors place upon anyone wishing to travel. Granted these factors are different for the walker, the car traveller, the sailor and the flier but there are certain basic aspects which are common to all. Even the serial killer labours under these constraints, as was brought home to me, almost forty years after my navigational training, when I was called in to help the police investigate the "Yorkshire Ripper" series of murders and assaults.

To consider what happened in the Ripper investigation the setting must now change from an idyllic summer in 1944 on an island in the Irish Sea, to a dismal winter in 1980, in the industrial West Riding of the County of York. The thought processes (despite being somewhat slowed by the ageing process), and the type of data used, remain essentially the same.

The Sceptical Witness

Chapter Six: The Yorkshire Ripper

At the end of November 1980 a serial killer who was dubbed the "Yorkshire Ripper" by the press, had been operating for at least five and a half years in the north of England. During this time he terrorised the female population to a degree which is hard to imagine so long after the events. Throughout this period a vast amount of police resources had been expended on the investigation and yet there was no indication that the assailant was any closer to being arrested than at the beginning of his series of attacks. Optimistic statements by some senior investigators such as "we know everything about the Yorkshire Ripper except his name and address" did not herald the apprehension of the killer, and public discontent, running at a high level for a long time, became extreme. Finally the decision was taken at top governmental level that the situation had gone on long enough and that a new approach to the long running and unsuccessful investigation must be prescribed. This intervention took the form of a decision to send in an independent group of senior investigators who had had no connection with the search for the Ripper. And so, on the 1 December 1980 a team of four senior police officers and one forensic scientist was despatched to Yorkshire. I was the forensic scientist.

At the time I was the Director of the Home Office Central Research Establishment, the only forensic science laboratory in the United Kingdom without a mainly operational function. Because of this I assumed I was chosen simply on the basis that, of all the laboratory directors, I was most easily spared from my job. The view of many of the overworked operational forensic scientists at the time was that research was an easy option to casework, crime scene examinations and court attendances. Later I learned that this was not the case at all and that the choice had been made by a member of Her Majesty's Inspectorate of Constabulary who, in his junior days, had been a detective sergeant on my very first murder case. Evidently, as my eldest brother always used to assure me, it is much better to know someone than to know something. Whatever the reason, I was pleased to be selected for the job, not least because I learned that my own boss would have liked the appointment for himself. I was going through a bad patch in my relationship with him at the time and, miserable creature that I was, the malicious streak in my nature took over (as unhappily it so often does at such times) and I delighted in the reports which I regularly received of his discomfiture in the matter. These despatches I received through the third parties which always exist in such circumstances. Human relationships are such that malice extended towards any particular individual is seldom unshared. Presumably public schoolboys, of which my boss was one, would have known how to behave better than did upgraded members of the proletariat, such as myself. But putting such human considerations aside we must return to the thread of the story.

Each of my four police colleagues was a detective of great experience and each came from a different police force. Furthermore each outranked the various investigating officers in the Ripper cases, a fact which removed many obstacles in our work. A disciplined service, such as the police, requires to be clearly rank conscious to function efficiently. At our temporary headquarters in the city of Leeds, we began to review the investigation as it had unfolded during the preceding five and a half years. Our aim was to recommend any change of direction in the pattern of inquiries which we felt to be necessary. Not that we had any executive power in forcing the adoption of such decisions, but there was little doubt that any report which we produced would be very influential.

On the date of the team's arrival in Yorkshire the crime series comprised 13 murders and 4 assaults. These were in a sequence which stretched from July 1975 to November 1980. The seventeen cases represented that group of attacks which most probably could be ascribed to the same assailant. However, as in all series crime investigations, there was uncertainty about whether some cases admitted to the series should be excluded, or others which had been omitted from the series should be incorporated. Nevertheless the seventeen cases represented the series as it was seen at the time by the investigators on the spot. At first I had some doubts about how our association with the investigation would work. Our group consisted of outsiders who would be attempting to right a situation which had become chronically unproductive, and it was inevitable that our reception by the local investigators would be somewhat muted. This was a perfectly natural reaction. Having laboured on the investigation for more than five years, the local detectives were hardly going to relish potential accolades for success going to a team imposed from outside. In a sense I was probably more easily acceptable to the local force than were my police colleagues, because I had previously worked as a forensic scientist in the district for a long time and I was well known to many of the police there. In the event things went remarkably smoothly, mainly due to the fact that my four police colleagues were all personable and greatly experienced senior crime investigators. All were blessed with high intelligence and each possessed a significant share of that most necessary characteristic of the accomplished police investigator, guile. It was decided that I, although not a police officer, would act as an equal and ordinary member of the group. I would have full access to all the information resulting from enquiries, irrespective of its origin. This meant I would be party to everything that transpired, and would not be limited to advising the group on the content of the laboratory reports in the seventeen cases. This proved to be a significant decision and it had a profound effect upon the provisional report which we issued 17 days after our arrival.

On the basis of the information that was available to us on our arrival in December 1980 the picture was as follows: the series of offences stretched from an assault in the town of Keighley on the 5th July 1975, to a murder in the city of Leeds on the 17th November 1980. In between these two crimes there ranged a series of fifteen other attacks which were believed to be the work of the same individual. Consequently the advisory group was faced with the problem of sifting masses of data, produced over a period of more than five years by many different police officers working over a wide geographical area under varying conditions. This sifting was an enormous task and it required many decisions to be made about which crimes should receive prior attention as being the ones most likely to yield useful information, and about the method of approach to be used by our small group. There was no question of trying to re-run such an mammoth investigation. It was a matter of identifying what we felt were the salient points of evidence and seeing if these fitted into any pattern which might provide new lines of enquiry for the investigation. We read all the case reports and many of the witness statements of the seventeen cases, and of some other "possible Ripper" cases. We interviewed all the senior investigating officers in the individual cases both from the standpoint of the case itself and of its position in the series as a whole. Work started at the breakfast table each day and continued until very late in the evening after which I fell into bed and slept soundly. The pattern was repeated the following day. Gradually a picture began to emerge. Although the attacker tended to choose prostitutes as his victims there were, particularly later in the series of assaults, some victims who certainly did not merit this description. The individual attacks tended to follow the same pattern. During the hours of darkness a woman would be approached and struck on the head with a hard instrument which in many cases, from the nature of the injuries, appeared to be a hammer. Thereafter the victim was stabbed to death, sometimes with a few, but often with many, blows. The first two victims survived the attacks but of the subsequent fifteen victims, thirteen died.

The amount and variety of the information to be absorbed by the individual members of the team was immense and under such conditions it would have been very easy for any thread of evidence to disappear into a fog of detail. The results from our interrogation of the many police officers who had been involved in the various cases, and occasionally of witnesses and surviving victims, was compared with what they had said in written statements often made years before. Regularly, both before and after these interrogations and readings, the group discussed the current picture and then refined their views on the best way to proceed. What follows now is several paragraphs of digression which, although they may break the flow of the narrative, might help towards its deeper understanding. Readers of a pragmatic inclination might do just as well to omit it and to take up the story several paragraphs further on.

Chapter Six: The Yorkshire Ripper

How do we come to "know" things? How does the human mind extract the general and the essential from the detailed and adventitious? Such problems have been grist to the philosopher's mill for at least the past two thousand years, but whether the results of their deliberations would prove of assistance in series murder investigations is a moot point. What happens, without any consideration of how it happens, is that the human mind tends to abstract a general and simplified picture of a complex situation in an attempt to explain the facts in the most reasonable way possible. This of course means "most reasonable" to an individual mind with its own compendium of foreknowledge and prejudice. The process is the same whether the thinker (in the most general sense of the word) is a police investigator, a research scientist, a lawyer, a doctor or any other member of the human race. Without considering the mechanics of how the brain does it, a mass of information is considered, some of it is distilled out as "evidence" and an explanation is thus produced for why a particular and disparate assortment of facts is associated together.

This explanation can be called a "hypothesis", a "hunch", a "theory", a "fact" or a "prejudice" according to one's point of view. Faced with a complex problem one may immediately ascribe the cause to an individual, an institution, a law of nature, a personal characteristic or to an act of God, according to one's mental capacity, taste or purpose. But the competent investigator, of whatever variety, is distinguished from the naive and uncritical inquirer in that once he has formed a hypothesis (which is the word I prefer to use) then he goes on to test it. He searches for facts which, if established, will tend to support the hypothesis. The best way he can do this is to search for facts which are potentially capable of falsifying the hypothesis. This is simply another way of saying that the facts must be relevant. If a murder suspect has been seen close to the scene of the crime about the time of the offence, then this is relevant precisely because the antithetical case is possible. An example of the antithetical case might take the form of reliable evidence that the suspect was several hundred miles away at the time of the murder, or imprisoned, or otherwise disqualified from being the killer.

The Sceptical Witness

All this may appear to be irritatingly elementary to some but profoundly obscure to others, but since it is the key element in all matters of judgement I take the risk of reiterating it. "Risk" because such topics put the writer in peril of losing readers at this point. But if practical matters such as both the remote and immediate causes of war, murder, disease and crime are to be resolved it is just as well to be conscious of what is the overall pattern of reasoning.

Returning to the Yorkshire Ripper, and to our two-week session of reading statements and case reports, of visiting scenes of crime and interrogating investigators, a general picture of the situation began to emerge. Firstly we refined the picture by ridding it of what we considered to be irrelevancies, and these included one belief which had been the linchpin of some very concentrated inquiries. This was the belief that the killer was a native of the town of Sunderland in northeast England. This belief had arisen because the chief investigating officer, a year prior to our becoming involved in the investigation, had received three letters and a tape recording. These communications, apparently from the same individual, derided the lack of success of the investigators and contained comments based upon information which, the chief investigator believed, only the killer would know. The tape recorded voice had a distinctive English regional accent which, in the view of both professional phoneticians and of local residents, was characteristic of the town of Sunderland in northeast England.

To most of the inhabitants of the United Kingdom this accent would appear to be classifiable under the general heading of "Geordie". So "a Geordie accent" had been adopted as a categoric eliminator in the latter part of the investigation. The "official" view now was that if a suspect did not have a Geordie accent then he could not be the Yorkshire Ripper. On examining this decision the advisory team concluded that it was an unsafe basis upon which to conduct the investigation. This was because all the information in the letters and the tape recording would have been available to any member of the public who searched the media with sufficient application. It must be said that this view was not restricted to the advisory team. It was also held by

Chapter Six: The Yorkshire Ripper

many experienced officers employed in the investigation. But the removal of this incubus to the investigation threw open our field of inquiry relating to both the origin and base of activity of the Yorkshire Ripper.

For the purpose of this account none of the other factors which we excluded need be discussed here although they were very important in shaping our thinking. Within the refined picture produced by two weeks hard work I shall emphasise only those elements which I found particularly significant, given my wartime navigational background. But in limiting the remainder of the story to "navigational" aspects I do not wish to imply that they were separate from the main review. The navigational tests that I applied were to ideas that were the product of the refining process applied by the advisory group as a whole.

So we were faced by a series of 17 crimes which had been ascribed to the same person, styled the "Yorkshire Ripper" by the Press. Thousands of people had been interviewed during the investigation and an unspecified, but much smaller number, had been subjected to a vigorous interrogation as suspects. Of the seventeen cases, fourteen had occurred in Yorkshire and the other three in Lancashire. A more precise distribution is Bradford (4 cases), Halifax (2 cases), Huddersfield (1 case), Keighley (1 case), Leeds (6 cases), Manchester (2 cases), Preston (1 case). I obtained the map locations and timings of each of these 17 crimes. The map locations were precise because they were simply where the body was found in the case of the murders, or where the assaults took place when the victim survived. The timings of the attacks in some cases, however, were less precise than the locations. Because of this, in those cases where the body was not found for some time after death, I simply adopted the convention of "time last seen alive".

To all this data I decided to apply the mind of the navigator to see if it would yield any indication of the base of operations of the Yorkshire Ripper on the assumption that, throughout the series, he had used the same starting point. I decided to use two methods. One was to calculate the "centre of gravity" of the individual locations of the attacks. The other was to examine the time of day of the attacks, irrespective of date, to see if this revealed any pattern likely to be useful in the investigation. Other approaches would have been possible and, with the wisdom granted to me by hindsight, I might have proceeded differently had there been longer to think about the matter. But the conditions in an hotel bedroom, or a police office, are hardly ideal for reflective thought, and time was short. Come to think about it, the shortcomings were to some degree those faced by a wartime bomber navigator.

The "centre of gravity" approach can be easily understood, in principle, by imagining some fairly common distribution problems. Imagine the warehouse for a network of supermarkets or the fuel dump for a group of bomber airfields. What are the criteria for positioning the warehouse, or the fuel dump, for minimum travel overall? Nowadays sophisticated computer methods are used to solve such problems but this must not be allowed to obscure the elementary fact that, in principle, the problem is easily conceived in simple mechanical terms. Imagine a map with the individual supermarket positions marked on it. Now visualise choosing a position for the warehouse, by eye, somewhere near the centre of the cluster of supermarkets. Mark all the positions so identified by using map pins. Now join each supermarket position with the warehouse by a piece of taut thread. Measure the total length of thread used. Now choose another position for the warehouse and repeat the exercise. Do this several times. The amount of thread used in each exercise will vary but the warehouse position that uses the least thread lies at the centre of gravity of the cluster of warehouses.

This elementary treatment of the problem is one that will attract the sniffs of the specialists or, if they feel strongly about it, their rage. Nothing inflames the specialist more than the interfering outsider who implies that their problems are conceptually simple ones. It is easy for the expert to point out situations in which the simple model falls down but this does not reduce the basic usefulness of the elementary "first principles" approach. One could write a whole book about the relationship such models have with reality. No doubt hundreds of books have already been written on the subject. But I am in danger of being led astray into a bout of specialist baiting. We must return to the substantive problem of the point from where the Yorkshire Ripper operated during his five and a half year series of attacks.

The centre of gravity of the Ripper attacks was established not with pins and threads but on the computer at my own laboratory. First, all seventeen crime locations were considered as a group on the assumption that they were all crimes committed by the same man. Next, certain of the "doubtful" members of the series were excluded from the examined group, in various combinations, and the reduced group of crime locations submitted to the same treatment. The six sets of crime locations which resulted from six separate sets of assumptions showed that the focus for the Ripper crimes lay in the region of Leeds and Bradford with a somewhat stronger indication of Bradford than Leeds.

Obviously the method could have been refined further by considering road distances instead of distances as the crow flies but this would have introduced other problems into the calculations. The number of refinements which could have been introduced into the exercise is very large, each requiring its own set of assumptions. If one looks at a map one can see that road distances approximate more to crow flying distances the longer the journey involved, so that probably little inaccuracy was introduced by using crow-flying distances.

The perceptive reader will realise that it had to be a possibility that the Ripper had chosen the location of his attacks deliberately to mislead the police as to his base of operations. This we realised at the time but also to be kept in mind was the requirement, from the standpoint of the attacker, to return to base as soon as possible after any attack and before police activity had been stimulated by the incident being reported. A serial killer is as subject to the constraints of time and distance as much as anyone. Furthermore he is restricted by the necessity to keep a plausible explanation ready should he be found and questioned by the police after an attack, and before regaining his base.

Because the Ripper needed darkness for his attacks I then decided to examine the timings of the assaults and see if they bore any relation to distances. It was evident on examining the data that the longer the day length the later the attacks tended to be. This was logical because the Ripper would have to wait longer for darkness in the summer months. But, even allowing for this correlation it was evident that the later attacks tended to be in the Leeds and Bradford area. In order to minimise the chance of detection after an attack was discovered the Ripper would have tended to attack later in the day the closer he was to home. The prospect of driving long distances on relatively unpopulated roads late at night, after carrying out an assault, would have doubtless been a factor in the choice of location of victim.

On the 10 December 1980 I wrote a short monograph for my police colleagues in which I argued for the Ripper's base of action being in the Manningham/Shipley area of Bradford. This idea was subsequently incorporated into the interim report for the Chief Constable of West Yorkshire which was produced on 17 December 1980. On Friday 2 January 1981 the Ripper was arrested in Sheffield by officers of the South Yorkshire Police but the reasons for his arrest were quite unconnected with our own investigations. It was then established that he, Peter William Sutcliffe, lived in the Heaton district of Bradford. Heaton lies midway between Manningham and Shipley.

An amusing (but only in retrospect) aspect of the story relates to how I learned about Sutcliffe's arrest. This occurred on Saturday 3 January when one of my police colleagues telephoned me with the news that "a Sheffield man" had been arrested for the Ripper offences. My dismay was immeasurable and I remember remarking to my wife "you are not only married to a fool but to one who writes his stupidity down on paper for all the world to see". Happily my misery turned to joy when the true story emerged. Interfaces alter cases.

Chapter Six: The Yorkshire Ripper

There are many possible ways of treating the time and location data in the Yorkshire Ripper and similar cases and I would doubtless have proceeded differently had I had more time to think. Some thoughts on the matter appear in the book mentioned at the end of this chapter. Even as I write this text it occurs to me that, if my theory of "the later in the day the closer to home" were the correct one, then I should have carried out centre of gravity studies on restricted numbers of the "late cases". For example, had I looked for the centre of gravity of the five attacks which occurred after midnight (Leeds(2), Bradford(2), Keighley(1) then the centre of the triangle formed by the three towns falls almost exactly on Heaton, the home of the Ripper.

All this emphasises the basic logical structure of imaginative enquiry. This is the "what if?" approach. "What would be the logical consequences of a provisional assumption that such and such is the case?" In this particular case the provisional assumption, or hypothesis, is that "the later in the day the attack took place, then the closer to home is the attacker". This gives results that can be tested by further enquiry. We start by looking at effects (clues) and considering their possible causes. We start by considering the locations of the late attacks and then asking ourselves why? The results from doing this supported the idea that the Ripper was a local man. One can at least hope that our report to the Chief Constable would have led to the concentration of enquiries into the Manningham/Shipley area of Bradford and that this would have led to the arrest of the Ripper. But in real life the intellectual and logical course of reasoning can be overtaken by unforeseen events. Just as it was in this case.

At 10.50pm on Friday 2 January 1981, Sergeant Robert Ring and Constable Robert John Hydes of the South Yorkshire Police were on motor patrol duty in the city of Sheffield. There they questioned, and later arrested, Peter William Sutcliffe. Sutcliffe was subsequently charged with and convicted of, inter alia, sixteen of the seventeen crimes which had been the subject of examination by our small group a few weeks previously. Sergeant Ring and Constable Hyde were described by the press, and deservingly so, as "The most famous policemen in the world". Their major accomplishment was that they halted the long career of a ruthless killer. One of their minor successes was that, in doing so, they proved that we were right in our recommendations.

Since the time of the Yorkshire Ripper investigation many academic papers have been published on the subject of the navigational aspects of serial crime. The names used for such studies are variable ("Geoforensics" and "Crime Spatial Dynamics" are just two) but they treat essentially the same problem. But whatever virtue such systems may possess must be established solely by their predictive power. This means going out on a limb before the event, betting on a hypothesis so to speak. It is insufficient to seek to demonstrate that had such and such a method been used then the "correct" result would have been obtained. Hindsightology, although a powerful method, is insufficient by itself. As Kirkegaard said "life can only be understood backwards but has to be lived forwards".

Cases such as the Yorkshire Ripper also raise the vexed question of "can the forensic scientist be both a hunter and an arbiter?" Most scientific involvement in criminal cases is corroborative rather than inceptive and the overwhelming attitude of my colleagues during my service was one of total independence from the police. I remember listening to a colleague lecturing on his involvement with the police in gathering evidence in an illicit drug manufacturing case. His own input to the investigation was both critical and necessary and the case was a resounding success. Yet several times during the lecture he was moved to express his disquiet at having to be a member of the hunt.

He was not alone in this attitude. Years ago I was involved in a murder investigation in which the investigating officer had located a single very good suspect. He was convinced the suspect was on the point of confessing and just needed a little prodding for the floodgates of confession to open. To help in this he asked me to play a theatrical part. Would I please don a white coat and examine the suspect's hands and fingernails slowly, deliberately and meticulously? Doubtless the investigating officer was partly motivated by the fact that many people find me dour and intimidating. In this way he hoped that the suspect would

Chapter Six: The Yorkshire Ripper

crack. He never found out if his ploy would work because I refused to cooperate. Theatricals were never my strong point and I considered such an involvement to be highly unprofessional. This was many years ago and attitudes change. If I were still working as a forensic scientist and a similar request were made to me now I would accept and play my part with commitment. Obviously if the circumstances haven't changed then I must have done so. I would not attempt to justify my change of attitude but only ask those concerned to think hard about the place of the individual in society. Certainly by the time I became involved in the Yorkshire Ripper investigation I was quite content to be a member of the hunt.

At the beginning of my 17 day involvement in the Ripper case, partly described in this chapter, I was sitting with three of my police colleagues in a police car parked on a bridge over the M1 motorway in Yorkshire. It was night-time and the sky was bright with the sodium lighting of the industrial West Riding. We were discussing the difficult task which faced us. After a while we fell silent and looked out of the car at the illuminated skyline. Suddenly one of my police colleagues said quietly "well, you're out there somewhere, chummy". I barely restrained myself from shouting "yes, and we'll get you, you murdering bastard". But such emotions are unscientific. So I didn't.

Now we shall return to the war.

Footnote.

The above chapter represents a partial account of my pre-arrest involvement in the Yorkshire Ripper investigation. All the factual information involved has already been published, with the agreement of the Home Office, in my book "The Scientific Investigation of Crime" (1987, Forensic Science Services Ltd, ISBN 0-9512584-0-0). The book is now out of print and so those interested in studying such matters further must obtain a copy from a library or other institution. Subsequent to the above involvement, and after Peter William Sutcliffe had been convicted and sentenced, I was one of a team which reviewed the whole Ripper investigation. The findings of the review team were presented to the Home Secretary in December 1981 ("The Yorkshire Ripper Case, review of the police investigation by Lawrence Byford Esq., Her Majesty's Inspector of Constabulary"). This chapter in no way depends upon the *post facto* material contained in the latter publication.

The Sceptical Witness

Chapter Seven: Fear and Fraud

From the near idyllic conditions on the Isle of Man I returned to wartime mainland England to continue my training as an air navigator. The prospect of getting mixed up in dangerous ventures loomed ever closer but, as a typical nineteen-year old, I paid little attention to this, being more concerned with the immediate requirements of the schooling and flying which filled my days, and the social life which filled my evenings. Life still remained some sort of game, a series of fascinating pastimes wherein I acted the central part and the war played a supporting role.

At an "Operational Training Unit" I was "crewed up" with five other airmen to form a six member crew of a twin engined Wellington bomber. These sturdy aircraft had seen service earlier in the war in operations but, at this stage of the war, they were used mainly for training aircrews. The crewing up procedure must have resembled a Victorian agricultural fair where farmers hired their help for the coming year. The various "trades" were gathered in self-conscious groups; gunners, wireless operators, navigators and bomb aimers and the individual pilots moved among them, selecting individual specialists and asking if they would care to make up a crew with him. There was no compulsion. I don't know what would have happened if a pilot had failed to find a full crew willing to serve with him.

It was very much a hit and miss affair. Presumably nowadays one would undergo endless psychological tests for compatibility before making such life dependent decisions. What criteria my own skipper used in selection I have no idea. There certainly seemed to be no identifiable similarities amongst us. The same applied to all the other crews on the course with one exception. Here the pilot was a very short man. Indeed he must have been perilously close to the minimum height for admission to aircrew. In his case he managed to assemble a crew of the same height as himself and, thereafter, this crew provided a cheerful miniature reflection of the other, long-limbed, crews on the course. But, systematic choice or not, the selection procedure seemed to work rather well and, during the time my own crew spent together, I cannot recollect any antipathies developing amongst us. Perhaps we were all aware that the future could be very short for us and there was no time to waste on personal differences.

It was only on my next, and last, training station that the idea of personal danger first intruded into my daily thoughts. At this airfield we had the task of converting our flying procedures from the two engined Wellington to the four engined Lancaster. This required an additional member of crew, a flight engineer, to take some of the routine load of control movements from the pilot. The flight engineer's seat was at the right hand side of the pilot and, watching them together one day, I suddenly realised that the back of the pilot's seat carried heavy armour plating whereas that of the flight engineer did not. Indeed the pilot's seat carried the only piece of armour in the entire aircraft as far as I could see. The rest of us had to put up with whatever fortuitous protection the design of the Lancaster provided and that was very little. The aircraft had been designed simply as a bomb carrying machine and superfluous weight was strictly avoided.

It was an interesting reflection of the division of labour in the crew and of the fact that, despite each member of the crew having a very important function to perform, it might be possible for the aircraft to get home without any one of them, given a lot of luck, with the sole exception of the pilot. He was the *sine qua non* of the crew. He warranted his piece of armour plating. I remember comparing the jobs of the various members of the crew and wondering how well I would do in each. My conclusion was that, for me, I was in the right job. I knew I had the power of concentration on mental problems in distracting circumstances and I knew that my own efforts would help greatly towards my own safety. On the other hand I did not know how I would fare as a gunner under attack, or as a pilot wrestling with a damaged aircraft and having to make instant life and death decisions. Yes I was in the right job.

One night, as part of our final practice for bombing operations over Europe, we were required to take part in a diversionary flight over the North Sea, to a point which was a bare 50 miles distant from the

Chapter Seven: Fear and Fraud

north German coast. The purpose of this flight was to mislead the German air defences into believing that the target was somewhere other than it was, thus drawing nightfighter attention away from the main bomber stream to the decoy. We were the decoy.

Before take-off a last minute fault developed in the radar navigational equipment on my Lancaster aircraft and I reported this to the captain. He called flying control on the radio and asked for someone to come out and fix it. Sitting in the aircraft at the dispersal point, with the engines yet to be started, all was quiet and peaceful and it was not long before the radar mechanic joined us in the aircraft. He clattered up the fuselage to join me in the navigator's position, carrying his tool kit. He was a young man of about my own age and he sat beside me and started to chat as he fixed my equipment. In a short time the repair job was done and the mechanic replaced the tools in his bag and got up to go. "Good-bye" he said. Then, after a short hesitation, he added "and good luck". Then he disappeared down the fuselage back to the safety of the workshops. This was a revelation. It was the first time anyone had said "good luck" before a flight and suddenly I realised that this flight would be different. My person was about to be imperilled by exposure to the enemy on his own ground, or at least, over his own waters. True the risks were not great. The chances of German nightfighters venturing out to sea to head off what might have been the main bomber stream were fairly small, but they were there.

From this moment all enjoyment went out of flying and I concentrated exclusively on optimising my own chances of survival. Although British bomber losses were much fewer at this time than they had been earlier in the war, flying over enemy territory was still a most hazardous business. I began to wonder why I had ever let myself get into such a fix.

Our five hour diversionary flight, centred on midnight, on the 20/21 February 1945, passed without incident and I remember my thankfulness when, on the way back home, I was able to report to the pilot that we were crossing the English coast at Cromer, a small holiday town in Norfolk. Shortly after this flight we were posted to our final station, an operational Lancaster squadron, at Mildenhall in Suffolk. Here I experienced three months of a life lived under conditions of emotional high tension, all the time wondering how it was that the other six members of my crew appeared so unaffected by it all. None appeared to be as terrified as I was and I fervently hoped they did not notice what a craven navigator they had as a crewmate. Fortunately our skipper was an excellent pilot, an Australian who had already fought in the army in the Far East before changing over to flying, in order to experience another sort of danger. "An old head on young shoulders" was how the bomb aimer described him to me. The bomb aimer was in a position to judge because, at thirty one, he was an old man and by far the oldest member of the crew. The rest of us, with the sole exception of the skipper who knew better, called him "Dad".

Our Australian skipper was cool, calm and competent in everything he did. In addition he was a compassionate man and I remember with shame an incident over Germany, in brilliant sunshine and amidst heavy anti aircraft fire, when the Lancaster next to us was shot down. As it plunged to destruction I heard the skipper's voice over the intercomm. "Poor bastards" he said softly, his concerns, as always, with others. My reaction was one of anger. "Fuck them" I screamed, "just you bother about us you stupid bastard"! My fear-generated rage evaporated as quickly as it had appeared and I noticed with relief that my microphone was switched off.

Our operational flights were, like all such flights, tense experiences. We bombed both at night and during the day. I preferred the nighttime. At night we were on our own and the pilot flew the course I told him to. Survival was very much an individual affair. During day time things were different. The Lancaster had been designed as a night bomber and was only lightly armed. This meant that it was easy prey for German fighters under most circumstances during daylight. However at this stage of the war there were not so many German fighters about. Because of this we flew in tight daylight formation with my function being reduced to that of checking the work of the lead navigator, and of issuing instructions to the bomb aimer as we bombed on the information on my radar screen.

Our protective umbrella at this time was a remarkable fighter aircraft, the Mustang. Flown by RAF and USAF pilots, and powered by the ubiquitous Merlin engine, these long range fighters were the main reason that Bomber Command was able to operate in daylight during the closing stages of the war. The Mustangs kept the remaining German fighters away and provided a feeling of relative security to us in the bomber formations below. The "relative" part related to what might have attacked us from above. As to attack from ground based anti aircraft fire the Germans never seemed short of ammunition when my valuable person was around. Each shell burst seemed to be a silent puff of grey smoke as the sound of its explosion was swamped by the chronic noise of a line of four Merlin engines. Even the nearby shell bursts seemed to be no more than muffled thuds to our deafened ears. Years later the permanent damage of such auditory abuse was nicknamed "Lancaster Ear". I have two.

Our three months operational experience was completed by dropping food supplies to the starving civil population of Holland at the end of April 1945. Then, during May, we made a group of trips to France to pick up released British prisoners of war. These flights were a happy finale to a war in which, despite often flying through heavy fire, and losing comrades, the gods remained with us and we never even scratched the paint of our aircraft. But even among these final pleasurable and relaxed flights, which provided such a contrast to the bombing raids, there was one bizarre incident which I have never forgotten.

We were flying on a northerly track, at very low altitude, over the city of Rotterdam on a pleasant day in late April, 1945. Although the Germans were still in occupation, a safe passage had been arranged by which it was agreed that they would not fire on the Lancasters which, at near rooftop height in broad daylight, would have been sitting ducks for the German anti aircraft guns. Inside our closed bomb doors we carried, in place of the usual bomb load, sacks containing food supplies. The bomb aimer had the task of ensuring that these dropped within the designated dropping zone. The target was a large open park in the city and, at a height of a hundred feet or so, our group of aircraft approached it as slowly as safe flying requirements allowed. I had no immediate duties so I was watching the proceedings with interest, waving enthusiastically in reply to the nurses on the roof of a large hospital adjacent to the dropping zone. A great crowd encircled the open space as the bombers flew in and I watched the sacks dropping from our companion Lancasters. Then I noticed a single figure running from the crowd into the hail of falling sacks, unable to wait until the danger had passed. He was struck by a sack and lay motionless and obviously dead. He had lived for several years under the foreign occupation of his country, had avoided death by violence and starvation, and was finally killed by a falling sack of food in the first hours of impending freedom.

When operational flying ceased we were kept busy training, but things were different. We knew we were just filling time and the sense of tension and urgency disappeared to leave the training flights just as an unwelcome and useless chore. "Fighter affiliation" was one of these training exercises. In this activity a Spitfire made mock attacks on us and our pilot threw the Lancaster around the sky in a gut wrenching ballet of avoidance actions. I heard the tail gunner chant his warning, (which we had never heard in earnest when we were on operations) "tail-to-pilot-fighter-fighter-starboard-quarter-up-corkscrew-starboard...GO!" Then I really noticed the difference. For the first time in several hundred hours of flying, I was air sick. The misery of my airsickness was compounded when we landed after the exercise. The ground crew refused to clean up the vomit and I had to clean it up for myself. Had it been an operational flight the ground crew would have done it for me without complaint. The war had truly ended.

With the arrival of victory there was the problem of great numbers of servicemen clamouring to be released from the forces. On the basis of first in first out I had to wait for eighteen months before I was due for release. During this time I said goodbye to my crew as it was dis-

Chapter Seven: Fear and Fraud

persed, each of us to be employed on a variety of time filling jobs. Our skipper went home to Australia and to his job as a school teacher. He was a superb gentleman, a fine pilot and a mother hen to his crew. I missed him greatly, probably because he had all those desirable qualities in his character which were so sadly missing in my own. For myself I began to think of what I was going to do on my release into civilian life and I suddenly realised that I was singularly unfitted to do anything that would lead to a worthwhile career. Half educated, and already at the age of twenty, I had to do something about it quickly. I decided to use the remainder of my service to try to remedy my lack of learning. Aided by the fact that former aircrew members had a large degree of choice of how to spend their waiting time, I started to educate myself up to university entrance level.

This I did by buying the necessary books and secreting myself in whichever empty building was available on whatever station I happened to be at the time. In this way, deserted buildings, which at one time had been the busy operational centres of war, became the private schoolrooms of a lone and feverishly self educating young airman. Sometimes I felt as though I was sharing my schoolrooms with the ghosts of those, my contemporaries, who had not survived the war. But in general it seemed to be a benevolent sharing. I felt a sort of ambience which said "good luck to you mate, we are pleased you survived". I was very pleased about the fact myself. My self teaching paid off and, just before demobilisation, I successfully sat the special university entrance examination for wartime servicemen. Fortified by my precious pass certificate I made application to enter University College Nottingham, scene of so many of my earlier hazardous exploits. They refused me. Their rejection letter told me quite bluntly that I was a "poor candidate" and they did not feel disposed to accept me. However, continued the letter, should I wish to pursue my application then I would have to sit their own entrance examination. Enraged by being referred to as a "poor candidate" I returned to concentrated study for several months, managed to pass the special entrance examination and so I gained admission to university.

The Sceptical Witness

My four and a half years' study at university was a happy time although, in common with many ex service students, I wasted too much time and drank far too much. There was still the lasting feeling of relief that we had survived the war and, given the opportunity, we repeatedly celebrated the fact. Because I was inspired by a vague desire to better the lot of the starving millions of the world's population, I took up studies in biology and chemistry. I had a hazy idea of entering agricultural research and making two ears of corn grow where only one had grown before. I graduated with a fairly poor degree which was not surprising because I recollect that during much of finals I was suffering from hangovers. Nevertheless fortune smiled on me and I received the offer of a research grant to study for a doctorate, which I accepted. The research topic in question was a fascinating one and very relevant to the substantial element of microbiology in my undergraduate studies. My new job was to examine the action of microorganisms on a substance used widely in the food industry, alginic acid, extracted from seaweed. *Prima facie* this may not appear to be an exceptionally riveting issue but it was, in fact, a most interesting subject for any biologist concerned with the teeming submicroscopic world of these minute creatures.

In this investigation I took over a project already started by another postgraduate student who had changed his interest from science to politics. As a condition of receiving the final instalment of his research grant, he was required to produce a report on the work he had completed until then. This account was to provide me with a basis upon which to restart the project. When I received the write-up I read it with great care, not wishing to repeat that part of the work which had already been adequately done. I was in for a shock. Scientifically naive I still believed implicitly in the standard image of the independent scientist who laboured with impeccably honest application to his work, in the spirit of a disinterested and unprejudiced search for the truth. A few weeks experimentation showed me that my predecessor's report of his investigations was nothing more than a well written text of pure fiction. It was just the sort of document that one might produce as a speculation upon the direction which a research topic might have fol-

Chapter Seven: Fear and Fraud

lowed, had it been undertaken. My investigations falsified my predecessor's laboratory results so conclusively that it was impossible to believe that the experiments he described had been done at all. Anxious to find out the reason for this I tried to make contact with him. He was still on campus but all my efforts to find him were unsuccessful and my messages remained unanswered. I still hadn't cornered him when I was told that he had departed to a fresh career elsewhere and so the mystery was never solved.

So I returned to the laboratory bench where I restarted the project from scratch. Things went very well and within a few months I had the draft of my first scientific paper ready to be vetted prior to publication. This was to be done by the professor, whose research student I was. Sadly, like the heads of so many university science departments, my chief was too busy sitting on committees, and chasing after research grants, to have much time for research topics of a minor nature such as my own. Nevertheless I managed to fix an appointment with him and I proudly took him the script of an article that I believed would firmly establish me on the pathway to a full-time career in scientific research.

At first he listened patiently to the description of my findings but, after a while, his lips tightened a little and thereafter his attention seemed to wander. Nevertheless he took the script from me and promised to read it and give his views. I returned to the laboratory bench and took up my work again but it didn't seem to progress as swiftly as before. I think I was using too much of my attention waiting for the return of the script so that I could get on, publish it, and collect my modest portion of scientific fame. I never saw the script again. As a result of this omission society was deprived forever of my research findings. I doubt if the advance of civilisation was slowed down very much by the default but, for me, the failure was a minor tragedy. Because the professor was so busy, my inquiries on the matter met with silence. Nevertheless several weeks after our meeting I finally received a document from him. This was the announcement of a job vacancy in forensic science, together with the professor's suggestion that I might like to apply for it. I didn't like, and I bluntly told him so, rather in the manner of the uncouth youth that I undoubtedly was. But, after a further few days during which I thought the matter over, I decided that perhaps my future lay elsewhere than in that particular department. So I changed my mind and, after a successful interview, I was appointed biologist at the Home Office North Eastern Region Forensic Science Laboratory at Wakefield. This I considered to be a temporary expedient while I searched for another job in research. The "temporary expedient" was to last for thirty years.

Twenty five years after the start of my employment in forensic science my early and short university career was to stand me in very good stead. I had become the Director of the Home Office Central Research Establishment which was the official research wing of the forensic science laboratories in England and Wales. Unofficially it also seemed to discharge the same function for most of the forensic science laboratories of the world because it was the only unit of its kind in existence. Part of our job at CRE was to research into new laboratory methods which were potentially of value in operational forensic science laboratories. These methods were either produced in CRE itself or they were selected from published accounts in the scientific press and vetted for their usefulness. I was already aware of the existence of some, potentially very valuable, experimental findings by two research workers in Italy. These results had come to my notice during my previous appointment as director of an operational laboratory but, in the very limited experimentation that we had time for in a casework laboratory, it proved impossible to confirm what the Italians claimed.

The claims related to the individual characteristics of human body fluids such as semen and saliva. It appeared, according to the Italians, that certain new factors which they had discovered would allow an augmented degree of individualisation of these fluids. Because the question of "individualisation" or "characterisation" of human tissue in all its forms is the main stock in trade of the forensic biologist, the Italian work attracted much interest.

Chapter Seven: Fear and Fraud

Semen and saliva are two body fluids of much importance in forensic science because they may be transferred in cases of assault, particularly those of a sexual nature. Anything which allows the forensic scientist to recognise those factors in the human body which are fixed and invariable in the individual, but show a tendency to differ between individuals, can yield very useful information to the investigating officer and subsequently evidence to the court. A familiar example of such factors is the ABO blood groups and, wonderful product of modern scientific research, the methods of characterising individuals by their DNA make-up. But we are talking of times long before the advent of DNA methods. What the Italian research claimed to show was the following:

Human semen and saliva can be classified into four different, and hitherto unknown, groups. Each human being belongs to one, and only one, of these four groups. If the individual is male then his semen and saliva must belong to one, and only one, of the four groups. If the individual is female her saliva (females do not produce semen) likewise belongs to one, and only one, of the four groups.

This was the kernel of the Italian claim for the discovery of what was, potentially, a very useful tool for forensic scientists. If a rape suspect differed in semen group, by this method, from the semen found on the female victim, then he could not have produced that semen. That is to say he was eliminated as a source of the semen on the victim. If the semen group proved to be the same then he could be, although he was not necessarily, the source of the semen. There was an apparent added bonus to the Italian findings. The technique they used required only a very modest capital outlay for equipment. This meant that laboratories in the poorer countries could hope to use the method within their tight financial limits. But we soon came across a snag. No laboratory in the United Kingdom could confirm the Italian findings. Not a single British forensic scientist could get the method to work. The four types of body fluids, as they were so carefully described by the Italians, appeared to be non-existent. But few scientists like to publish nil results. If one scientist says that such and such a phenomenon can be proved to exist by the use of such and such a method then, *prima facie,* other scientists believe him. Thereafter, if a scientist fails to find the described phenomenon then he tends to believe that the fault lies with himself in that he has reproduced the experimental conditions wrongly.

This is more of a problem in the biological sciences than in the physical sciences because of the complexity of biological systems. There is much more to go wrong in a biology experiment than in a physics experiment. Had the reviewing scientist meticulously carried out the experiments according to the discoverer's instructions, and found "something", but a "something" different from that which the discoverer found, then that would certainly be worth publishing. But to follow all the procedures meticulously and then find nothing at all simply smacks of failure.

Look at it this way. If a prospector comes back from an expedition and states that there is gold in the hills, and describes where it is to be found, others may take him at his word and go to look for themselves. If they fail to find any gold they may or may not conclude that there is none to be had. If, on the other hand, they follow their informant's instructions and locate a deposit of copper pyrites ("fool's gold") in the expected spot then they are likely to conclude that their informant was simply wrong and they would cease looking further. This is different from finding nothing at all and then harbouring the nagging feeling that the gold may be have been there, but was missed. Analogies such as these are useful secondary aids for thinking through a problem but they should not be pushed too far.

But to return to the substantive problem, the failure to confirm the Italian work remained the situation over a period of several years during which time the Italians produced a series of papers on the subject, which confirmed and expanded their original findings. Moreover during this period one laboratory in the United States, and another in Japan, "confirmed" the experiments of the Italian workers and discoursed at length on the underlying nature of the newly discovered factors. Yet, for the scientific world at large, the problem remained one of deep and impenetrable mystery. At last some new evidence came to light. Two British laboratories produced experimental results which seemed to show that, had the alleged body fluid varieties existed, then the Italians must have spotted another phenomenon which they had not reported. Resorting to analogy once more the situation was similar to that of the suspect for a crime who claims, as an alibi, that he was in a particular cinema at a particular time and saw a particular film but fails to mention some important collateral detail. Had he truly been at the cinema he could hardly have failed to notice, say, a breakdown of the projection equipment, or a major disturbance in the auditorium, or a fire alarm. This cast a new light on things. At long last it seemed a solution to the mystery was at hand.

It still seemed to us that fraud was not a possibility because the two Italian scientists who had produced the research findings (and they had also applied them in case work) had expressed a willingness to come over and demonstrate the method in my own laboratory. This was no trivial offer. To demonstrate a new scientific method in a difficult field is an onerous enough task as it is. If, in addition, one requires the demonstration to be in someone else's laboratory, with unfamiliar equipment, in a foreign country and using a foreign language, then one can only admire the resolution and self confidence of the demonstrators. So I invited them over to my own laboratory to perform the demonstration. There were two of them, a professor and his research assistant. The professor's facility with the English language was good enough to awaken the usual amazement in our Anglo-Saxon community that anyone could speak a foreign language so well. The research assistant spoke little English but, with the help of his chief as interpreter when available, and the ability of scientists of all nations to communicate by sign language and figures when discussing their own field of research, things seemed to go along quite well.

We set up the research assistant with a bench in a convenient laboratory and ensured everything was as near to his liking as possible. Then, over a period of several days we watched, as best as the human faculty of attention would allow, the manipulations of the research assistant. These proved to follow exactly the procedures as published by the Italians themselves. So, what were the results?

In four demonstrations the method appeared to work twice, and to fail twice. So the demonstration of the method was equivocal. This was very disappointing because it did not decide the issue either way. But, at least, the visit provided the basis for joint experiments. So we arranged further scientific co-operation in the hope that we might finally resolve the issue. The two Italian scientists took labelled samples of saliva, from several members of the laboratory staff, back to Italy. These samples they grouped in their own system and then they returned the findings to us. Later, as a disguised test, we sent another batch of saliva samples to Italy from two members of our laboratory staff. These two scientists were members of the same set of individuals who had been tested previously by the Italians and had already been ascribed their "groups" in the new system. But, as part of the new exercise at this stage, we made an important modification to the experiment. Unknown to the Italian scientists we took the saliva from one of the two samples submitted for retest and we divided it into three parts. One part we labelled with the correct name. The second and third parts were given false names. The net effect of this manipulation was to submit a total of four samples, bearing four different names, from two individuals. Two were labelled correctly and two were labelled falsely. Obviously if the Italian system gave consistent outcomes then it should have returned the same results from the three samples taken from one person but labelled with different names. In the event the results, when they were received, showed that the three samples of saliva from the same individual, (two of which bore false names), had been ascribed to three different groups.

Here was unequivocal evidence that the Italian researchers, barring errors, were incapable of doing in their own laboratory, and under their own experimental conditions, that which they claimed to be able to do. Even though the method of exposing their shortcomings was Machiavellian I believe that it was entirely appropriate, given the circumstances. Nevertheless I think that most of my staff involved in the matter felt uncomfortable about the method that I dictated. I had no such qualms. Had the method involved been a genuinely effective one then the three saliva samples from the one individual must have been identified as belonging to the same group. They were not, and the results left the Italian scientists with a good deal of explaining to do.

Any further investigation of the disparities was cut short by the untimely death of the main experimental worker involved. This was a tragedy. He was a comparatively young man and, in the normal course of events, he could have expected an indefinite career in the specialist experimental field that he appeared to have pioneered, but it was not to be.

How did this all happen? Nowadays scientists are not so queasy about discussing scientific deception and there are even full-time university workers, and specialist publications, dedicated to the subject. Much scientific work depends upon sequential research grants that are conditional upon the success of a particular line of investigation. "No success, no grant" would appear to be an entirely reasonable way of spending public money. Nevertheless any initially successful investigation carries an increasing risk of reluctance to accept the results, or non-results, of experiments which suggest that the inceptive experimental findings themselves were wrong. Under such circumstances there is a danger that desperation may lead to a lack of discrimination. When payment of the household bills depends upon continuing a string of "positive" findings, then it becomes easy to see only what one desires to see. This is not something peculiar to science. In its extreme form it is homologous, not just analogous, to the drowning man who clutches at a straw. Such dangers are obviously more pressing in those cases where there is only one worker who is doing the relevant experiments in his own intimate corner of the laboratory. If there is sparse critical assessment of his results from his scientific managers then the perils are intensified.

And what of those scientists who "confirmed" the findings of the Italians? Such "confirmation" was a spin off from the original series of published papers. If one reads a ten-year series of scientific articles, adulating and advocating a particular scientific discovery and its consequential merits, then there is an almost overwhelming tendency to believe that "there must be something in it". For the uncritical this belief can take the place of confirmatory experiment and so the process can start all over again.

It is a measure of the power of the published scientific word that, even given the chain of events described above, a large part of the forensic science community tended to think that something substantive must exist even if it was overlain by a burden of experimental misinterpretation. When we published the final account of our overall findings (not including the experiment containing our own deception in the matter of sample labels) my own choice of title contained the term "scientific myth". I was prevailed upon, by the other signatories of the article, to change this to "scientific enigma". They obviously still thought that "there must be something in it"

But in using misleading sample labels was I not placing myself in as questionable a moral position as those whom I believed were deceiving us? This objection I think is met by the fact that I declared our deception the moment the experiment was completed. Furthermore our procedure only encapsulated a much wider and subsequently well established practice, pioneered by British forensic science laboratories, known as the "undeclared test". This can involve setting up entire criminal "cases" which are then submitted to forensic science laboratories, through the normal police channels, in the guise of real crimes. In this way the performances of individual scientists and laboratories can be assessed in the hope that the scientists involved will carry out their investigations in ignorance of the fact that they are being tested. Even though it follows that the shrewd, the sceptical and the aware will come out of the tests better than their more naive companions for reasons collateral to the case examinations themselves this, in a sense, might be accepted as part of the test itself. But we are getting on to

Chapter Seven: Fear and Fraud

very debatable territory. Perhaps the possibilities of scientific deception should form an integral part of the training of all scientists. Certainly my own early experience of the practice made me much more sceptical of the notion of scientific high-mindedness which was current at that time.

Then perhaps I am being ingenuous. Possibly the awareness of the existence of fraud in scientific research was more widespread at the time than I believed. Perhaps most of my scientific colleagues simply didn't think there was anything to be gained by "shouting about it" and that things would right themselves in time. After all , the idea that truth will prevail is sounder in the physical world than elsewhere in human affairs. I can agree with them in one respect. My life would have been much more tranquil had I held similar beliefs.

The Sceptical Witness

Chapter Eight: An Eminent Scientist

I now return to the main narrative thread of my story, some twenty five years previously, on my first day as a forensic scientist. At the time I viewed my departure from university as nothing more than a temporary absence from the groves of academe. The sight of my first forensic science laboratory did nothing to deflect me from that view.

I arrived at the North Eastern Forensic Science Laboratory in Wakefield on the first of April 1952. It was a cold , drizzly, and dismal day which, together with a suspicion that fate had maliciously chosen All Fools Day for me to start my new job, combined to put me in a gloomy frame of mind. The appearance of the laboratory didn't help much either. It was located in Bishopgarth, the old palace of the Bishop of Wakefield, an ornate but depressing red brick structure with steeply pitched blue slate roofs which glistened dully in the drizzle. The entrance driveway was a mass of little lakes through which I carefully picked my way on foot to arrive at a massive front door. Inside I found an architecture which had been designed for a more prayerful and reflective occupation than for one dealing with the physical traces of murder, rape and arson and similar human misdemeanours. The laboratory shared the building with the department of the County Prosecuting Solicitor but scientists and lawyers were quite cut off from each other. A large central entrance hall was surrounded by a periphery of smaller rooms some of which now provided the laboratory accommodation. This was in the form of a linear series of chambers to which a new access had been made from inside the palace entrance porch.

Because the biology department was half way along this sequence of rooms it provided a path between the chemistry department on the one hand and the physics department on the other. Consequently we were never short of company of one sort or another. Such an arrangement would not be tolerated nowadays for reasons of case integrity and sample security. But at that time forensic science was still feeling its way towards optimum practices in the field of criminal justice. Upon my arrival the plan was for my appointment as "staff biologist" to overlap with that of my predecessor for a period of one month. The reasoning behind this move was to give him time to introduce me to my job and to allow him to smooth away any initial difficulties which I might encounter. He should have been well qualified to do this because he had been a forensic biologist for a good number of years, broken only by his war service as a navigating officer aboard a Royal Navy destroyer. He was one of the most charming men I have ever met. Tall, slim and blond he wore a permanently quizzical expression which displayed the fact that the world, as he saw it, was a matter for total puzzlement. Unfortunately that also appeared to be the case with his relationship with forensic science.

He was utterly disorganised. Whatever order there appeared to be in the section resulted from the fact that his technicians worked quite independently of him. They carried out their examinations of the materials submitted by the police and produced the results of their investigations which they then placed before their boss for him to report upon. I never saw him do any bench work himself. When he received the results from his assistants he seemed to view them with the same puzzlement as that with which he viewed the world at large but, somehow, he managed to write reports which were subsequently tendered in court. Happily for him, if not for me, his incomprehension of the world did not prevent him enjoying life to the full and it soon became evident that his entire existence was carefully tailored to his own social needs. His immediate and all consuming desire was to leave the Wakefield laboratory and to arrive at his new posting in London. It was there that all his intimates lived and worked and it was the only place where life could be lived to the full. For him Yorkshire remained a *terra incognita*, a foreign land to which he had been banished by a malicious Fate for its own secret and malevolent reasons.

Stories told about him were legion, but I shall restrict myself to just one. It was a Friday in summer and he was looking forward to catching the earliest train possible to London for the weekend. He was due to give evidence at court in the morning but, on arrival there, he was told that the case had been postponed to another day. Seizing his opportunity he hurried back to Wakefield, swiftly packed his weekend

Chapter Eight: An Eminent Scientist

bag and went to the railway station. From the station, ignoring the fact that he was required back at the laboratory to check and sign some pressing reports, he telephoned the laboratory and said that he was held up at court and would not be returning to the laboratory that day. Unfortunately for him, as he spoke, a train whistled quite clearly down the telephone line and a second or so later the same whistle drifted through the open laboratory window to be heard quite clearly by the police liaison officer who was taking the call.

The liaison officer immediately took the waiting reports and drove over to the railway station half a mile away and just caught our hero as he was about to embark. Totally unfazed by the detection of his subterfuge the offender signed the reports, and waved a cheery goodbye to the liaison officer. He left laboratory affairs to look after themselves as he went happily towards his weekend in London. It soon became obvious to me that even our short overlap period of one month was onerous to him and it was not long before he had inserted the idea into the director's mind that I, the new chief biologist, was an excellent chap of prime intellect and unmatched technical and scientific brilliance. Because of this it was evident that his own continued presence, representing as it did the *ancien regime*, could only serve to stultify my native genius and arrest my scientific growth. He may not have used these actual words but it was most certainly the impression that he gave to the laboratory director.

His silver tongue worked, and soon the director came to me and asked if I required any more tutoring from my senior colleague before he was released to go to London. I replied that I doubted if I could learn any more about the job from the individual in question than he had taught me already. I omitted to add that this was because twice nothing is nothing. So off went my predecessor to London, both to his own delight and (so I was later told) to the profound dismay of his new director who had served with him of old. I was left behind, as the new chief biologist, basking in an undeserved reputation as a brilliant forensic scientist. The truth was that I was a total ignoramus who had been tossed in at the deep end and left to struggle to the bank as best I could. The laboratory director himself was in no position to judge my competence as a biologist because he was himself a former university professor of physical chemistry whose scientific knowledge of the living world and its products was minute. Happily my two assistants proved rather more knowledgeable and helpful than either their erstwhile boss or the director did and, with their help, I launched myself into the routine of a very busy forensic science laboratory. In truth the settling in procedure proved remarkably smooth and I was soon at home with most of the standard examination methods used which, being microscopical, were extensions of all the techniques I had been using regularly at university. I read voraciously, finding my texts wherever I could. At the time there was very little published which was explicitly on forensic science and I was soon to learn that what little there was had to be approached very judiciously and with great vigilance.

When I look back on those early days in forensic science I have to console myself with the thought that, in the development of all skills used by the human race, things are usually done badly before they are done well. As in all professions, practices used anciently would not be tolerated today. The crudeness of some of our methods would shock or amuse present day scientists but they were the forerunners of modern techniques and attitudes. Without them there would have been no progress. We represented an early stage of the onward march of science in the service of justice and, although present day forensic scientists may feel superior when they consider our forensically antediluvian fumblings, I am sure they are pleased that we were there to hack our way through the investigatory, legal and scientific undergrowth on our way to achieving the pre-eminent position that forensic science holds today.

My ambitions as a research scientist faded with the passage of time as the pressure of casework mounted. I found myself in the witness box within a week of my take-over, giving evidence on human bloodstains in a case of assault. This was a subject I knew precious little about and it soon became evident to me that there was no-one else in the labora-

Chapter Eight: An Eminent Scientist

tory who knew much about it either. The most experienced forensic scientist in the laboratory was the director and he would beat a hasty retreat to deal with administrative problems whenever questioned on a remotely biological subject. Yet it seemed that the gaps in his knowledge did not prevent him from attending court and giving evidence on almost any subject under the sun. In this he was not alone and I soon learned that some other laboratory directors also tended to be polymaths. To an extent this was explicable because it appeared to be what the public wanted. Cases where forensic scientists gave evidence were considered newsworthy, and newspapers inclined to stoke the cult of the individual. The appearance of the great forensic scientist Professor T. or Dr F. in the witness box signalled to the public that scientific justice was in course of being done and being seen to be done.

It was soon brought home to me just how widespread this attitude was when I attended court in one Yorkshire city. The case itself was an unremarkable one in which I gave evidence, and obtained my release from court before midday. Before I left the courthouse to catch my train back to the laboratory the police officer in the case came to me with a grin on his face. He told me that he had fixed it for me to go to lunch with the Lord Mayor in the city hall that day. After being assured it was not a joke I went to the lunch and sat at the top table with the Lord Mayor and other dignitaries in a large and ornate hall filled with about two hundred guests. It appeared that there was some special occasion under way and it was evident that the police officer really knew how to fix things. I felt a surge of gratitude towards him as I reaped the unexpected culinary harvest. Later I got to know just how well he had fixed things for me.

The lunch was excellent and I offered heartfelt but silent thanks to the local citizens who were paying for my unexpected treat as I tucked into the exquisite cuisine and the fine wines. What a wonderful meal it was for a young and impecunious scientist who normally would be lunching on a sandwich. The sandwiches, still in my brief case, were now strictly for the birds. With the eating finished, but with the wine

still flowing freely, I settled back comfortably to listen, rather somno-
lently, to the speeches by the dignitaries on the top table as they indulged in an orgy of amiable and mutual back slapping. These masters
of the municipality certainly appeared happy with the world and listening to them seemed to be a small enough price to pay for such a
wonderful meal. I listened with only a detached interest as the Lord
Mayor named the important guests and thanked each one for his wonderfully original contributions to the day's happy proceedings. However, he continued, he was happy to tell the assembled company that
the day was unusual in that we were honoured by an unexpected guest.
Amongst us, it appeared, was a world famous scholar who happened
to be visiting the city that day. Speaking from a note that had obviously been supplied to him, he then went on to give an outline of the
accomplishments of this paragon. These achievements (he was still
speaking from his note) were such as to match those of Darwin, Pas-
teur and Einstein all wrapped up into one. The Lord Mayor may not
have used those exact words (alcohol rots the memory and I was well
down my second bottle of wine) but that was certainly the overall
impression that I gained of this intellectual prodigy.

The distinguished visitor, the Lord Mayor continued, would perhaps
be willing to address a few words to the present assembly. I joined in
the tumultuous applause and cries of assent as I craned my neck and
peered down the top table wondering which of the prosperous diners
was the visiting scholar who was about to address us. Then, as if in a
nightmare, I heard the Lord Mayor speak my name. Silence fell and
cold terror gripped my entrails as I realised that everyone in the room
was looking at me with expressions of benevolent expectation. But I
had never before made an after-dinner speech in my life. In fact my
only experience of speaking in public was my limited court experience
and, in those cases, I always had a carefully prepared script to speak
from. But there was no way out. I had no choice but to heave myself to
my feet. This I reluctantly and unsteadily did, holding firmly on to
the table as I rose to more tumultuous applause, which gradually sub-
sided to complete silence as my audience settled expectantly to receive
their unforeseen treat from this most eminent scientist.

Chapter Eight: An Eminent Scientist

I looked around at the huge sea of expectant faces, my mouth was dry and my throat even drier as I tried to think of a few plausible comments which would not appear too banal to the audience. This should not have been difficult because the company was in such a good mood and so thoroughly wined and dined. I opened my mouth and no sound came out. I snatched for my water glass which, until that moment, had been contemptuously hidden behind my array of wine glasses and I gulped a large mouthful dispensed by a quivering hand. I sensed impending disaster and I began, mentally, to give up. But then something happened. I suddenly noticed, standing in the banqueting room main doorway, the police inspector who was responsible for my plight. He was leaning nonchalantly on the doorpost with his hands in his pockets and on his face was a sardonic expression. He seemed to be saying to me "you clever scientist chaps, you're all very well when you're standing up there in the witness box, or on the lecture rostrum, preaching your own narrow subject, but when the real flak begins to fly you're no damned good!"

"Oh yes I am" you bastard, I gritted through my teeth "and you are just about to see how good". My brain suddenly cleared and I was on an ice cold landscape where the assembled company was present, not as good drinking fellows, but as a herd to be bent to my will. Abruptly I was sober again as I began to speak. I told them of the position they and their city held in the history of Britain and of the world and that we, at that moment and in that place, were an integral and irreplaceable part of that developing cosmic pattern that permeated our small but unique corner of the universe. Theirs was the proud saga of human endeavour in the arts, in education, in industry, and particularly in my own field, that of science. They and I were one in this story of unfolding natural progress.

I went on for quite a while and began to enjoy myself. Suddenly I realised that I was capable of going on for a good deal longer but I still retained a modicum of prudence which counselled me to bring my disquisition to a polished end. After all, in the same way that belief conditions behaviour, so behaviour conditions belief, and I was beginning to convince myself that I was talking first class sense. So I thanked the Lord Mayor (to whom I bowed respectfully) and the assembled company for the unique benefaction they had bestowed on me that day by their presence. Then I sat down.

The applause was generous and we all took it as a signal to end anything that might be construed as formality and we all returned to drinking at John Citizen's expense. I recalled some time later that one of the assembled businessmen came to me afterwards and offered me a job but, since then, I've never been able to remember what it was. It was probably as a vacuum cleaner salesman or something of the sort. He was obviously capable of recognising someone who was able to lay it on thickly when the occasion demanded. Later I was solicitously transported by police car to the railway station and there gently deposited into my third class carriage (my Civil Service grade did not warrant first class travel) for the journey home. I learned a lesson that day. If you are ever offered a meal for nothing then be prepared to sing for your supper. There is no such thing as a free lunch, and you may be the one who is expected to pay. It was also my first experience of an attitude common among senior police officers. They tend to admire people who, upon finding themselves in an unexpected and difficult situation, manage to extricate themselves with credit. I subsequently found it not uncommon for such situations to be engineered for the amusement of the company. It is harrowing for the victim perhaps but is excellent training for anyone who has a job where it is necessary to "think upon your feet".

Those were the days of the small borough police forces and a local chief constable might have a strength of a hundred officers or less. Because of this procedures varied widely amongst different towns as they were tailored to local conventions and facilities. On one occasion I gave evidence in court in such a small town and, after the case, the police presented me with a box of kippers. How they came by them I don't know but they were a welcome adjunct to the parsimonious pay of a Civil Service Scientific Officer. I delightedly carried my large and smelly trophy home on the train to the discomfiture of my fellow passengers and to the delight of my wife who had the task of feeding a hungry husband and two growing children on a minuscule house-keeping allowance. I think we must have given some of the kippers away to friends. An entire boxful is a lot of kippers.

It was on another visit to the same town that the chief constable, on learning that I was new to the area, arranged for me to be taken on a sight-seeing tour by police car. The frankly grubby industrial surroundings were hardly the stuff to stimulate the artist or poet but the pride of the police car driver in his own small town was infectious and I soon began to see the same beauty that he obviously did and to appreciate the significance of the area in Britain's maritime history. Beauty is indeed in the eye of the beholder. It was a memorable trip. I noticed that the driver occasionally interrupted his eulogy as he kept in regular radio contact with his headquarters as we drove around. I also noticed that he was using the callsign "Lucy Two". I asked why this was so and he smiled and replied that Lucy was the name of the chief constable's wife. It appeared that all their small fleet of police cars was labelled Lucy One, Lucy Two, Lucy Three and so on. Evidently the chief constable thought a lot of his wife. This conclusion was borne out a few years later when I learned that Lucy had died and that after the funeral service, the chief constable, in his unbearable loneliness, had walked out into the grey waters of the North Sea to join her.

The variety of police forces was matched by the range of cases which we received for examination. Nowadays a police force has to think carefully before sending a case to the laboratory because of the high cost involved and because of the practice of individual pricing. The use of sophisticated scientific equipment, such as is common in the modern forensic science laboratory, requires a lot of financing. But in our pioneer days all was centrally funded through the government and we were at liberty to accept any case in which we thought we could render assistance. Indeed the problem was, in some cases, to get the wide range of police forces we served into the habit of using the laboratory. Almost any case was accepted solely upon the criterion of whether we believed we could help in solving the issue concerned. The question of whether the issue itself was worth pursuing in the first place was one which we left entirely to the police. In this way we accepted a wide variety of problems which were scientifically interesting even if socially trivial. They would not be entertained by a modern laboratory director.

One of these was the case of the Chief Constable's petrol tank. Here the samples submitted were four bottles of fluid. Three were labelled as being samples of urine, one from each of three individual police officers and the fourth was labelled as fluid from the petrol tank of the Chief constable's car. The problem was to determine which, if any, of the three officers had urinated into the chief constable's petrol tank. Such a problem might be solved today simply by examining the DNA content of the myriad of body cells to be found in urine. In those cells there would be found the genetic formula which, in nearly all cases, is peculiar to the individual. But the modern DNA techniques were not available at that time and we had to fall back on other methods.

In this we were fortunate in having on the staff an enthusiastic organic chemist of superb technical and scientific qualification and boundless enthusiasm for his work. He examined the problem by means of a technique which, at the time, was at the forefront of the advance of analytical chemistry. This was "paper chromatography" and it allowed him to develop a pattern of coloured spots on filter paper, from each of the four samples. These patterns in some degree represented the content of amino acids in the samples. Amino acids are the biological "bricks" which make the protein "buildings" of the human body, but we had little idea at the time of how amino acid content might vary amongst individual samples of human urine. In the event the three patterns from the urine differed to some degree from that of the fluid from the petrol tank. However one urine sample was more "similar" to the "crime sample" than the other two and the case was reported on this basis. Although several garbled tales filtered back from the police force concerned we never heard a definitive account of the outcome of the case.

Chapter Eight: An Eminent Scientist

This would perhaps be called a waste of laboratory time nowadays but it all added to the scientific expertise of the analyst concerned. Indeed the scientist involved in the case later became the world's leading authority in chemical toxicology and in his many cases, and his research work, he often used paper chromatography. So perhaps the officer who urinated into the chief constable's petrol tank helped our budding toxicologist to hone his skills as he progressed, through the years, from being an obscure junior scientist towards becoming the undisputed world leader in his subject. In life everything is connected to everything else.

Following the theme that there are always lessons to be learned from the most banal of experiences, I was early impressed by the extent to which some members of the human race will go to avoid anything that can classified as "work". One demonstration of this was the number of cases of the theft of sheet lead from church, shop and factory roofs which came into the laboratory. Often in such cases it was possible to show that sheet lead in the possession of a suspect came from a particular roof by matching up striations, cut marks, paint smears and much else and this explained our regular involvement in these cases. But even allowing for the fact that lead is a valuable metal, the profit received, matched against the effort expended, was very low. If one balanced the poor return gained from illicit sales against the risk of working secretly on a high roof at night, together with the physical effort of tearing the lead up and then transferring it quietly and secretly to where it could be sold, at a price much lower than the going market rate, then the profit was indeed small. It was not as if ordinary jobs were difficult to obtain, for these were days of high employment. Perhaps it was simply the spirit of the entrepreneur.

But the workshy did not concentrate entirely on stripping lead from roofs. Their ingenuity knew no bounds. In one of my cases I had the task of identifying material labelled as "Japanese Water Flowers" sold by a street pedlar on the main streets of a large Yorkshire city. The genuine article, it should be noted, consists of dried bits of coloured plant material which, when placed in water, expand to pretty flower-like structures. These objects were amongst the simple amusements of those comparatively unsophisticated days.

The printed instructions on the water flowers packet sold by the pedlar directed that the buyer should place the contents in water and then wait three hours for the results to appear. At the laboratory we found that the contents of the package were nothing other than cut up fragments of coloured "Pampas Grass" of the type used in dried flower arrangements. The small size of the fragments prevented instant identification by the buyers of the packets and the three hours specified in the instructions allowed the pedlar to depart with his takings before customer dissatisfaction was generated.

I learned to identify many types of dried fragments of plant material, mainly in cases of suspected possession of proscribed drugs. The wide range of synthetic drugs commonly used by the addict today, a consequence of something known as "progress", was not available then. This ability to identify small bits of the vegetable kingdom was, unlikely though it may seem, also useful in safe breaking cases. Safe-breaking cases were part of the regular input of work to the laboratory. Our evidence in such cases might relate striations on a damaged safe with the instrument alleged to have caused them which had been found in the possession of a suspect. Perhaps traces of the explosive used to blow a safe open might also be found on a suspect's clothing and so provide a link between the suspect and the scene. However my own particular input to such cases was mainly in another area.

Safe construction in those days was a fairly crude affair. There was an inner and outer casing to the safe, rather like the construction of a vacuum flask, and in the cavity between the two casings was a substance which was known as "safe ballast". This was a mixture of sawdust and alum crystals and the reputed reason for its use was that in case of fire the alum crystals would melt and release what is known as "water of crystallization". This would then provide a wet sheath to the contents of the safe and so minimise fire damage. I have no idea how effective the ballast was for its reputed purpose but it was certainly of value in another, probably unforeseen, application. This was because when an intruder opened a safe illegally, using either tools or explosives, the ballast tended to be spread about and, almost inevitably, some of it got attached to his clothing. Thereafter it was often my job to search the clothing of a suspect and compare any fragments found with a sample of safe ballast taken from the scene. It could be difficult for the defence to explain away, in court, the fact that the accused's clothing bore, say, traces of mahogany and pine sawdust mixed with alum crystals and that this was exactly the constitution of the safe ballast.

I developed a sneaking admiration for some of the exponents of unofficial safe opening because I admire good technical expertise in all the useful arts as long as they are not associated with violent acts against the individual. I admired them not because of their antisocial intent but because of the effectiveness of their methods. As in all fields of human endeavour there are both good and bad practitioners. I remember a feeling of compassion for one safe breaker who, after labouring long and hard, neatly blew the safe door off with explosive. The sole monetary content of the safe was a five pound note which, although not a huge reward for a night's labour, was worth possessing in those days. Unfortunately the force of the explosion blew the five pound note to bits. He was convicted and I felt a sneaking sympathy for him and I thought that the amusement of the police officer in the case was, perhaps, a little excessive.

But despite the kaleidoscopic range of cases I was expected to deal with, the main thrust of my work lay in the investigation of violent assaults, including rape and murder. In these cases the presence of stains of body fluids, particularly blood and semen, on the clothing of victim and suspects could be of great evidential value. The blood of the victim was often transferred to the clothing of the attacker and the semen of the attacker was often transferred to the person of the victim. These transferred traces could be critical factors in the evidence for the prosecution.

The Sceptical Witness

In the case of blood the procedure in laboratory examinations was first to establish that the stains on the clothing were, in fact, stains of blood. Some stains can masquerade as blood even to the practised eye. One of my early cases concerned extensive patches of what appeared to be blood which appeared on one of the greens of a golf course. The overall appearance of the scene was as if a body had lain on the green bleeding freely for some time before being removed. In fact I was able to prove first, by chemical tests, that blood was absent and then, by microscopic examination, that the red colour at the scene was caused by a colony of microscopic plants. Examinations such as these can forestall the police chasing off after red herrings.

If stains were confirmed as blood then our next step was to establish that the stains were of human origin or, if not, from which animal they originated. After all it would be of little evidential value if blood stains on the clothing of an accused person, in a case of violent assault, were admitted by the defence to be blood stains but claimed to be chicken blood. Thereafter we searched for features of the bloodstains which tended to characterise them as the blood of the victim or, conversely, to eliminate this possibility. This type of examination has advanced to a high degree of individualisation in modern times but in those days, over forty years ago, we were largely restricted to the identification of the common ABO blood groups. There are four of these and each human being belongs to one, and only one, group: A, B, AB or O. If the assailant and the victim belonged to the same ABO group, which occurred in about one case in three, then there was little one could do to take the characterisation of the blood any further by analysis of its intrinsic properties.

However, even where the blood of the accused and that of the victim could not be discriminated by grouping tests, there still remained the extrinsic properties of the stains to be considered in the form of their shape and distribution. It was often possible to show that the disposition of the bloodstains on a suspect's clothing were characteristic of those resulting from an assault. If a globule of blood travelling at speed strikes a surface then the final shape of the bloodstain so caused can

Chapter Eight: An Eminent Scientist

yield useful information on how it got there.

In ways such as these I became closely familiar with the physical results of acts of human violence. I suppose my sneaking regard (but not approval) for the expert non-violent criminal stems in part from my hatred of violence. Another reason is that I have always admired truly expert specialists, even in those fields which I would personally find routine and monotonous had I to become involved in them myself.

My work became inextricably tied up with the ideas of comparison, individuality and identification. The basic question which faced me was "did, or did not, the two features under examination come from the same source"? Were they of cognate origin? This key question is always complicated by the fact, known from experience, that no two physical phenomena witnessed by a single observer are identical. The events may have great similarity even to the extent of the observer being confident that they come from the same source but they are never identical. It may be that such differences as occur are simply differences in collateral features, properties which are supplementary to those which are indicative. That, of course, is the job of the expert diagnostician in all fields. He must decide which are the relevant and which the irrelevant features in any diagnostic situation. It is here that the dabbler, or even the specialist who ventures outside his own field, may fall down.

Perhaps the best example of this theme of the indicative and the collateral, even though it seldom figured in my casework, is the question of fingerprints. No experienced fingerprint specialist ever says that two given fingerprints are identical. He might say that he is confident that they come from the same individual, which is the essential point in question, but he knows that many collateral factors can affect the production of a fingerprint. But he also knows the difference between a feature which is of diagnostic value and one that is merely the product of contingent factors.

The Sceptical Witness

We also learned the paramount importance of performing a thorough visual examination of our samples before we applied any specialist laboratory tests. The story was widespread (although doubtless apocryphal) about the expert witness who was called to give evidence in a paint transfer case. He gave evidence that the fragments of paint found on the suspect's clothing, and the damaged paint at the scene of crime, gave identical results in all the highly technical laboratory tests he had applied to them. Unfortunately he omitted to mention that they were of different colours. Some varieties of the story added "because he hadn't noticed".

My own inexperience early led me to commit an error in identification which caused me great personal embarrassment. I had only been in my job for a few months when I blundered. The consequences of my error, acutely humiliating for me, served to increase my scepticism and my reluctance to accept the work of others at anything like face value. At the time I was still in the process of becoming informed about the many peculiar acts of human beings of which I had been ignorant but which were then, and probably still are, widespread. The background to the case was as follows.

In a country district of the North Riding of Yorkshire a police constable was cycling down a country lane in the early hours of the morning. It was very dark. On observing a light in a nearby farmyard he got off his bicycle and went to investigate. Looking through the window into an illuminated pig shed he saw a man standing on a stool and copulating with a large sow. He watched for a while and then went into the shed and arrested the man on a charge of bestiality. He arranged for a veterinary surgeon to take a vaginal swab from the sow and he then sent this in to the laboratory to see if there were any human semen on it. This may seem a little superfluous under the circumstances considering that he, the police officer in the case, had watched the act being performed for some time. But the accused man made no statement of admission and, in court, the trial could have resolved itself into a dispute between the word of the defendant and that of the police officer. So, independent corroboration was required in the form of the identification of human semen in the vaginal canal of the sow, if any were there.

The most important step in the laboratory examination was for me to examine the swab microscopically for human spermatozoa. These are the tiny tadpole like objects, each of which carries a well shuffled half set of those factors, the "genes", which characterise the human individual.

There were sperm on the swab from the vaginal canal of the sow but they had some features which did not appear characteristic of human sperm. Realising the possibility that the sperm could have come from a boar I checked in the only book in the tiny library of the laboratory which carried a diagram of what pig sperm should look like. This book was one of the classic texts in forensic medicine and it was written by a Regius Professor of Forensic Medicine, a man of great distinction. The spermatozoa from the sow looked nothing like the pig sperm figured in this distinguished text book. I felt that if I could eliminate the possibility of pig sperm then I would be justified in reporting human sperm since it appeared that there were no realistic alternatives to these two organisms. But I felt unhappy about doing this elimination on the basis of a picture in a textbook, no matter how distinguished the author. So I arranged to obtain a sample of genuine pig sperm from a veterinary centre. If this were to confirm what was pictured in the textbook then I could finally eliminate pig sperm and write a report to the court that human semen was present in the vaginal canal of the sow. Then I made a grave error.

The court date was approaching and pressure was placed upon me to write the report before I had made the final test because the police wished to complete their file. Initially I refused, but when the laboratory director suggested I was being arrogant in not accepting the evidence from what was probably the most eminent forensic medical textbook in existence, I agreed to write the report. A few days later I went to the magistrates court. There I gave evidence that I had found human semen on the swab taken from the vaginal canal of the sow.

The Sceptical Witness

The case was committed for full trial at York Assizes. A few days later the sample of pig semen arrived at the lab. I examined it and it immediately became apparent that what I had found on the swab was pig semen. The diagram in the eminent textbook was totally worthless and bore no relation to what occurred in nature. I went to the laboratory director and told him of my findings. He seemed oddly detached from the problem and anxious to get on with his other work, but he agreed with me when I said I proposed to send another report in which I would withdraw the findings in my first report.

My subsequent appearance in the witness box when I withdrew my evidence was pure misery for me. The prosecution barrister was furious when what appeared to be a totally sound case fell apart before his eyes and, despite there being an eyewitness to the event, the jury acquitted the accused. Thereafter I always had the feeling that the police officer in the case, whom I met subsequently on many professional occasions, viewed me as a half-wit.

He may have been right, but the incident taught me never to make the same mistake again by accepting eminent authority as a substitute for doing a full check myself. It was a fortunate fact that the case occurred early in my career. The earlier one learns important lessons the more significant those lessons are.

Chapter Nine: Murder, Rape and Arson

I soon learned to suppress any moral judgements I might have had on my cases and to concentrate as far as possible on the scientific and technical aspects. This was comparatively easy for me. I was so interested in laboratory work that there was little room in my thoughts for anything else, save for the wife, daughter and son I now had in my small family. Indeed I spent an inordinate length of time each day, both at work and at home, thinking through my cases and whatever small piece of research I had under way, of which there was always at least one. The trouble is that I was fascinated by the process of discovery. Whether it related to a criminal investigation, or to a bench experiment, I was enthralled by the work of finding out. This is an exhausting affliction and it usually leaves those damned by it with little energy for anything else. But it caused the time to pass quickly and interestingly during the working day even if it left me drained at the end of it.

Case specialisation was much less in evidence in forensic science laboratories in those days than in these. Early on I was expected to attend the scenes of factory and mill fires and to examine the carbonised residue for evidence of how the fires had started. I remember standing in the middle of one burnt out factory in south Yorkshire and asking myself what sort of job I had let myself in for. The steel framework of the building stood as a black skeleton from which dripped inky black drops of water from the firemen's hoses. Here and there were piles of sodden and blackened debris which the firemen were systematically turning to extinguish every last spark. And there I was, an "expert fire investigator", more concerned by the necessity to keep the soot off my only decent suit, rather than to discover the cause of the fire. I hadn't the least idea of what to do but I put on some sort of show, spoke at length to the firemen, and returned to the laboratory to write my report. I also returned with the determination to avoid such cases as far as I could in the future. They really were not my style. Happily I was soon successful in this and all the fire cases were taken over by a more willing colleague to whom I was truly and permanently grateful.

The Sceptical Witness

An amusing sequel to this experience occurred some twenty years later when I was director of the Northern Region Forensic Science Laboratory in Newcastle upon Tyne. Because we were such a small laboratory we were very much at the mercy of the pattern of case work and the contingent demands which were placed upon us by the local police forces. We had, so to speak, no slack which could be taken up in times of emergency. There were only three experienced fire examiners in the laboratory and, with the requirements of courts, scenes, leave and other factors, we were sometimes in the position of being asked to dispatch someone to the scene of a suspicious fire but having no-one available.

In one such case pressure was being placed upon me to send a scientist to a fire scene but I had no-one to send. Thinking about the problem as I walked down the laboratory corridor I saw a member of my staff approaching from the opposite direction. He was a very competent young chemist but he was inexperienced in fire scene examination. But stimulated by my own early experiences as a "fire examiner" the following exchange took place:

Director: M......, I want you to go to a fire at A........
M: But I am not a fire examiner
Director: I've got news for you.

This was the sum total of the victim's preparation for his visit to the scene of the fire, much the same as my own experience of twenty years before. But based upon this abrupt induction he went on, in the years following, to become an extremely able specialist in the field. To paraphrase a well known aphorism "Nothing sharpens a man's mind as much as the knowledge that he is shortly to appear in the witness box as an expert". Such methods of "training" specialists would be frowned upon in these modern times but they nevertheless had their benefits.

Although much of the work of the forensic scientist can be formal and corroborative, taking place after the arrest and charge of a suspect, in some cases the scientist becomes involved much earlier in the process. A good illustration of this is an early case in which I was involved.

Chapter Nine: Murder, Rape and Arson

A woman in her late eighties had been found naked and dead lying in the back yard of her terraced house, beneath a wide open bedroom sash window. The pathologist reported that the cause of death was the injuries related to a fall. So it appeared to be established that the deceased fell from the window to her death. There remained the question "did she fall or was she pushed?" Interviews of the deceased's neighbours suggested that the woman had been displaying some bizarre behaviour and she seemed to be becoming progressively senile. Because of this the local opinion tended to be that the deceased had been leaning out of the window and had fallen accidentally. Yet there were some associated circumstances which suggested that things were not as straightforward as they might be. On the tiled floor of the woman's kitchen there was a pile of household utensils and some attempt had obviously been made to set fire to them. Was this the result of senile behaviour or was there a more sinister explanation?

All the household objects were sent into the laboratory (I had not examined the scene) together with various post mortem samples which I set about examining. The first fact that emerged was that there was semen on the vaginal swab taken from the corpse. This, in itself, would not have established foul play although considering the woman's age it was a matter for suspicion. But what was even more interesting was the examination of a "posser" which had been found amongst the pile of objects on the kitchen floor. The posser was a long stick, about the same diameter as a broom handle, and on one end was a bell shaped object made of copper. This, in normal use, was plunged up and down in the wash tub to agitate the contents. Around the tip of the handle end I found semen together with a type of body cells which are characteristically found in the female vaginal canal.

From this it could be concluded that the woman had been penetrated during a sex act and that emission of semen had occurred into the vagina. Afterwards the posser had been inserted into the vagina and so had picked up traces of the semen and of cells from the vaginal canal walls. The only credible interpretation of these facts, the investigating officer felt, was that the woman had been subjected to a violent sexual assault and then killed by throwing her unconscious body out of the bedroom window.

At this stage of the laboratory examination the director intervened and said that he proposed to take my microscopical preparations, which established the above facts, to another laboratory where a much more experienced forensic biologist could examine them. I had no objection to this although, even on the basis of a few weeks' experience in forensic science, I was confident that my findings were correct. So, off went the laboratory director to London where my conclusions were duly confirmed. Thereupon the director said that he proposed to report the case himself which he proceeded to do. So, in my first murder case I never got to court, an omission which was repaired many times afterwards.

This case was interesting to me in a respect other than the laboratory findings and the director's actions. It demonstrated to me how crime investigations differ from laboratory analyses in one very important respect. The research scientist will commonly repeat an experiment as many times as he wishes because he assumes that he is experimenting against a background of circumstances, or natural laws, which do not change with time. But the background against which the investigator operates is always changing with time, and often very quickly. Evidence which may be easily available today may be difficult to obtain tomorrow and have disappeared irrevocably the day after.

In the case of the murder of the old lady the investigator had the scene examined for fingerprints, as was routine in such matters. Quite a large number of marks (fingerprint examiners tend to use the word "marks" for scene of crime prints) were discovered and most of these were eliminated as belonging to the victim herself, or to those with legitimate access to the house who were, in the opinion of the investigator, beyond suspicion. The process of examination and elimination of the prints took some days and finally there remained a single print from the scene which had not been eliminated. This, according to the fingerprint examiner, was a fairly recently deposited mark. The objective dating of such marks is fraught with difficulty but an experienced fingerprint specialist, after examining perhaps thousands of scene of crime marks, develops a feel for the age of the marks he examines. This is hardly strong enough evidence to be given in a court of law, but it is evidence good enough for the investigator to take into account during his enquiries. In this case the investigator, a very experienced man, made a key decision. He decided to treat the remaining, uneliminated, fingerprint as that of the killer and to design his investigation around that assumption.

He could have been wrong. The fingerprint could have come from someone who had legitimate access to the premises but was unknown to the neighbours or to the investigators. The fingerprint examiner could have been wrong (experts sometimes err) and the mark could have been an old one unrelated to the crime. But a decision had to be made.

Had the investigator made a wrong decision about the fingerprint and embarked upon an expensive and fruitless mass fingerprinting programme, and then information had come to light that his decision was wrong, he would have received little sympathy. Had he made a mistake then the reasons why he did so would be plainly evident to those who can only work something out when they know the result before they start. But having made the decision the investigator followed it up with its consequent enquiries and he ordered a mass fingerprinting programme. Furthermore, because the killing took place in a barracks town, he directed that the first persons to be fingerprinted should be the military. This was because the forces personnel were far more mobile than the civilian population. Any soldiers posted to a new station elsewhere, before fingerprinting, would cause a heavy drain on resources because of the necessity to locate them individually and deal with them through local police forces. In the event, after a relatively small number of individuals had been fingerprinted, the crime scene finger print was matched with that of a soldier at the local barracks He was subsequently convicted of the murder.

The Sceptical Witness

Although the above case is an example of the scientist producing inceptive evidence, rather than evidence which is only corroborative, the case was rather unusual. The police attitude to forensic science then was largely that the forensic scientist was there to corroborate the evidence already gathered by the police. I experienced several examples of police exasperation where my evidence tended to negate details of an already established police case. It was felt in such cases that I was being less than helpful in disputing that which was "obviously true".

In one case of murder the victim had been struck down by a single stab wound in the back at waist level. The knife went in through the woman's black plastic belt and, from the examination of the cut mark, it became obvious that the weapon used was a broad, thin bladed, two edged instrument. But, from somewhere adjacent to the murder scene, the police recovered a commando style knife which was unbloodstained and had a diamond shaped outline. They became convinced that this was the weapon used in the attack, a view which was partly facilitated by an equivocal report by the pathologist on the nature of the entrance wound in the body. The case was never solved and the true nature of the weapon was never fully established. My own reputation with that particular police force was not high because of my failure to confirm what was "obviously true".

Somewhat later in my career I was faced with a case of assault where the nature of the weapon used had been established by the full confession of the attacker, but yet again I had to dispute the "facts". In this incident, which was not without its amusing aspects, the victim had been papering the ceiling of his kitchen whilst standing on a stepladder. While in this position he entered upon an argument with his wife who terminated the dispute by stabbing her husband in the abdomen. Immediately contrite, she called the ambulance, then the police, and then she made a full written confession of her crime. She handed over to the police the weapon which she said she had used in the attack. Because it is not unknown in such cases for the assailant to withdraw a confession, the police required some independent evidence to support their case and so they sought laboratory assistance.

Chapter Nine: Murder, Rape and Arson

Laboratory examination showed that a single stab cut in the abdomen region of the victim's clothing had been made with a very sharp one edged blade. It had penetrated two layers of thick worsted outer garments, then a knitted woollen jumper and finally two layers of heavy woollen underwear. The knife produced as the weapon of assault by the victim's wife was a round ended, blunt edged butter knife which was quite incapable of cutting any fabric, even when wielded most vigorously. When I pointed this out to the officer in charge of the case he became exasperated. The woman had confessed and handed over the weapon of assault so why did I wish to throw a scientific spanner into a smoothly functioning prosecution machine? Nevertheless I persisted and, with ill grace, he returned to the scene where he recovered a sharp carving knife from a drawer in the kitchen. This knife exactly matched the cuts in the clothing. Furthermore the blade bore a heavy longitudinal streaking of human blood which was of the same blood group as the victim. This was obviously the knife which had been used. Why had the wife falsified her confession on a single detail? This question I shall leave to the psychologically informed.

The changed police attitude is nowadays almost complete. The British police now view forensic science as an independent judicial entity rather than as an arm of the investigation dedicated to confirming preformed police opinions. Indeed it has possibly gone too far in the direction of what might be called academicism in that the scientist can only distance himself from the police to a limited degree if his help is going to have maximum effectiveness. Some comments on this will be made later in the book but for the moment I will give just one further example of the old police view.

In my first month's service as a very green forensic scientist I was involved in the investigation of the death, from head injuries, of a young man who was travelling on a train. Independent evidence showed that he received his injuries when he leaned too far out of the compartment window and struck his head on steel scaffolding erected at the entrance to a railway tunnel.

The Sceptical Witness

We had two police liaison officers attached to the laboratory at the time. These were police officers who had been detached from their parent forces and placed under the authority of the laboratory director. Their function was, nominally, to educate the local police forces in the value of forensic science to the police investigation, and to answer questions about police practices and procedures when asked by their scientific colleagues. In practice their activities tended to widen somewhat and they were employed in other directions, including that of scene visiting. In the case in question the police liaison officer had examined the location of the alleged railway accident and had recovered a tuft of hair from the scaffolding. He brought this to the laboratory and I compared it under the microscope with head hair recovered from the deceased at the post mortem examination. It was a good match, as far as a tyro forensic scientist could see, and I was helped by the fact that it was a rather distinctive ginger colour. I reported the match and my written report was read out at the inquest, which I did not attend. A verdict of accidental death was returned and this was doubtless the correct one, having regard to the available eye witness evidence.

Many years later I was thinking about this case, visualising the samples in my mind's eye when I suddenly realised that the hair samples had been set up to give the required result of confirming what was "obviously true". Sharpened by many years' experience of hair examination it became plain to me, in retrospect, that the sample allegedly removed from the scaffolding had in all probability been simply a part of the sample taken at post mortem, with a false label. Personally I have no doubt that this action was taken to prove the "effectiveness" of the laboratory's services to the police and the falsification, in its results, did no harm at all. Nevertheless it illustrates very well the attitude adopted by some police officers in early forensic science. It is perhaps just as well I didn't get to know at the time that I had been set up. My rage at being used as a scientific puppet by someone else, and my inborn lack of reticence, would probably have deprived a well meaning young police officer of his job, and my own laboratory of much of its burgeoning reputation of independence from the police.

Chapter Nine: Murder, Rape and Arson

In those days of early forensic science the pattern of cases that came into the laboratory reflected more the analytical capabilities of the laboratory rather than the operational requirements of the police. For example during my first year's service I noted the fact that we received a torrent of cases dealing with the suspected arson of haystacks and I wondered why. Perhaps there were bands of incendiarists roaming the fields of north east England, firing haystacks at every opportunity. Later, when I had time to think about the matter it occurred to me that the cases followed closely upon the publication of a new laboratory analytical technique which gave some assistance in deciding if the combustion was spontaneous or not. This article had been written by a well known (one would more often say "eminent" in those days) forensic scientist and had been widely publicised. Thus it gave the police a chance to appear up to date and for the chief constable to be able to write in his annual report that his force has used the lab during the year. Remember the average lab in those days serviced a dozen or twenty police forces rather than the four or five that it might do today. Only the exclusively urban forces would not have experienced stack fires during the year.

About twenty years later I was in conversation with a colleague from a large European country which was beginning to develop forensic science facilities. I asked him if his police forces used these facilities very much and he replied "only as a public relations exercise". So it would appear that my early experience was of a natural stage in the development of the use of forensic science by police forces. But, returning to the stack fires, the question posed to the laboratory was to determine if the stack had been fired maliciously or if it was simply a case of spontaneous combustion. In most cases this was evident from the examination of the haystack *in situ* and one of my colleagues spent a substantial part of his time visiting farms for this purpose. If it was evident that the fire started from the outside of the stack then that was an indication of arson. If it started from the inside then it was a sign of spontaneous combustion. Another good piece of evidence was the smell. A spontaneously fired stack has a highly distinctive odour.

Farming methods in those days were comparatively primitive compared with present day practices and a farmer might stack his hay before it was dry. This gave a good breeding place for bacteria and other micro-organisms which multiplied in the centre of the stack, generating heat to the extent that a runaway temperature rise was initiated. The sight of smoke issuing from a stack tended to exacerbate the situation because of the tendency of farm staff to rake their way to the centre of combustion. Unfortunately doing this only led to more air being admitted to the hot stack centre and a conflagration resulted. Faced with such a situation a farmer might choose to believe that the fire resulted from arson rather than from the bad practice of stacking damp hay, knowing that insurers do not pay out on the latter. So a complaint of arson was made to the police and this is where the laboratory became involved.

The laboratory method used in such cases was to measure the acidity of samples of partly burnt hay. Fermentation in the presence of a restricted supply of air, such as was the situation at the centre of a damp haystack, led to the production of a large amount of acid in much the same way that milk sours. A laboratory report to this effect relieved the police of the task of searching for a non-existent arsonist and the insurers from paying out on the results of the farmer's own negligence.

The commonest type of case in which the laboratory was concerned was DUI, a shorthand for "driving under the influence of alcohol to such an extent as to be incapable of having proper control of a motor vehicle". In these cases we measured the concentration of alcohol present in the urine (less often in the blood) of an offending driver. There was no statutory alcohol limit at that time and benches of magistrates, and juries, tended to require the urine alcohol concentration to be converted into the amount of beer or spirits one would have to drink to reach such a level. This was done by a (biologically speaking) highly dubious method which gave the benefit of a substantial doubt to the defendant. Benches of magistrates composed of miners or mill workers were hardly likely to be impressed by a calculated intake of only three or four pints of beer even in those cases where the defendant was

Chapter Nine: Murder, Rape and Arson

found helplessly drunk at the wheel of his car. But it was much better than nothing and it paved the way, years later, for the acceptance of the view that what mattered was the concentration of alcohol in the blood of the drinking driver, not the amount he might have drunk. Nowadays, of course, there are statutory alcohol limits, in the same way as there are statutory speed limits. I did comparatively few of these cases myself but I was often present in court, waiting for my own cases, when they came before the bench or, less often, before a jury. The pattern of evidence was always the same . The police officer would give evidence of arrest, the police surgeon would follow with evidence of his examination of the defendant at the police station and the forensic scientist would then give evidence of his analyses and calculations.

The final prosecution question to the police surgeon went as follows:

Prosecution advocate: "And what opinion did you form doctor?"

Police Surgeon: "I formed the view that the defendant was under the influence of alcohol to such an extent as to be incapable of having proper control of a motor vehicle".

This, of course, was the wording of the charge and it contravened the basic rule of English criminal procedure that no witness was permitted to express his opinion upon the guilt or innocence of the accused. That was entirely a matter for the bench or the jury. I sometimes used to tax my lawyer colleagues with this basic anomaly but I seldom got any reply which would satisfy a logician. On one occasion when I asked a solicitor who was very experienced in the prosecution of these cases what he would do if the defence objected to the police surgeon giving his opinion regarding "under the influence of alcohol" he replied as follows: "I would reframe the question and ask "Doctor, if in a case, other than this one, you had found the same results upon examining the defendant as you have found in this case, what would you then say?" Lawyers are incorrigible.

The Sceptical Witness

Since every police force had its own police surgeon, the county and larger city forces more than one, their experience varied greatly. Some police surgeons might get to court only once or twice a year but others could give evidence two or three times in a working day. One of the latter, whom I subsequently got to know very well, organised his court appearances to near perfection. Because his office was in the same building as the court he arranged that he was only called into court when his evidence was imminently required. In this way he was able to carry out useful work in his surgery without hanging about interminably in the witnesses' waiting room. I remember feeling envious about this because I always begrudged time "wasted" in court as I waited for my own cases to be called. My laboratory was always miles away from the court and such flexibility was impossible in my own cases. Later on in my career I realised that my time had not been wasted and that my long witness waiting room conversations with detectives, pathologists, police surgeons and lawyers made me a more rounded forensic scientist than one who might have spent nearly all his time at the laboratory bench.

A spark which started this process of realisation occurred one dreary morning at an Assize court in a large and drab Yorkshire city. It was Monday and I had already spent the whole of the previous week at the court during which I had disposed only of two of the large clutch of cases which filled my brief case. Moreover the cases involved were of the formal and unexciting kind which, though necessary in the chain of evidence, seldom provoked any interesting cross examination. I was starting the week profoundly fed up and feeling rather like an anonymous item in a complex and illogical process from which, should I suddenly disappear, my absence would hardly be noticed. Verging on self pity, and faced with the likelihood of spending many more days at court, I began to think regretfully of the research career I had abandoned because of my contretemps with the professor. As an academic I would have been master of my own time, and of my own procedures, instead of being a mere appendage of what I was beginning to regard as an anachronistic and ramshackle machine, the English legal system. Neither did it escape my notice that just about every other professional associated with the court was far better paid than I. Resentment began to mix with the self pity and I began to curse my own stupidity for allowing myself to get into such a fix. I really should have kept my mouth shut and not got up my professor's academic nose by being such a smart alec. The groves of academe had never looked so attractive as they did on that grey and miserable Monday morning. A damp and dispirited forensic scientist awaited his calls into the witness box to give his formal evidence. Then the trumpets sounded.

These were the trumpets that sounded each morning during the sittings of the Assize court as the two high court judges, magnificent figures in scarlet and ermine robes, descended from their Rolls Royce and solemnly mounted the stone steps at the front of the court house. It was always the same procedure in this city where the local corporation really had a flair for such matters, perhaps as an antidote to industrial grime. They hired two trumpeters from the orchestra at the local variety theatre to play valved posthorns at each assize. The trumpeters were very, very good. Not only were they good musicians but they unfailingly exercised their Yorkshire wit and took great trouble to choose a fanfare that was appropriate to each occasion.

Thus one judge who had not visited the assize for some time, although previously a regular on the bench, was delighted to be welcomed with a formal fanfare which suddenly modulated into the opening bars of "Ilkley Moor baht 'at".

Where 'ast tha bin since I saw thee?

His pleasure at being recognised and welcomed in such a way was evident and I've no doubt that there might have been a defendant or two that day who profited from the good judge's pleasure.

On another occasion a judge arrived at the assize court on his birthday. He was welcomed with the strains of "Happy Birthday to You" which then, as he reached the top of the steps, modulated into a few bars of "He's a Fine Old English Gentleman". Some said that there were tears in the old man's eyes. Once more a good day for defendants.

But such memories of these occasions made no impression on me that day. Although I have always appreciated something done with spirit and style, and the judges' fanfares were good examples of these, the weight of the case files in my briefcase, and the prospect of another dreary week at court, deepened my gloom as I sat in the corridor looking at the crowds of dejected humanity milling around me. I glanced along the corridor and saw the two judges enter the main door, turn and bow to each other, then proceed in opposite directions to their respective courts. One judge approached me and I reluctantly folded my newspaper and heaved myself to my feet to stand and respectfully await his passing, a minor and unnoticed pawn in the great man's judicial day.

This particular judge was a small and courteous man before whom I had often given evidence. He walked slowly and with a marked limp, a lasting consequence of war. As was usual for English High Court judges he was accompanied by an associate, a man who wore a black tailcoat and pin striped trousers and carried something that looked like a billiard cue. It was doubtless of some ceremonial significance but I never found out what. The scarlet of the judge's robes was the only patch of bright colour as he made his way down the long corridor between two rows of drab and cheerless plebeians towards the spot where I stood amongst them, impatiently waiting for him to pass so that I could sit down and resume my place and my newspaper as a bored appendage to the English legal system. Then a miracle happened.

A few yards away from me the judge turned to his associate and I heard him say "Why look, there is Mr Kind". Shortly afterwards he drew level with me and stopped. He then turned slowly to me, smiled and bowed deeply. Then he bade me good morning. I bowed and returned his compliment and watched as he moved on and entered court. At that moment, quite coincidentally, the sun came out and shone through the high clerestory windows of the corridor, giving

Chapter Nine: Murder, Rape and Arson

light on to the assembled masses and bestowing a colour to their cheeks and a sparkle to their miens. Then I realised that they were all staring at me. "Who is this guy?" they seemed to be saying "this nondescript, lanky fellow in the shabby suit? He really must be somebody very important. Just imagine, being bowed to by an English scarlet judge!".

And so I became important. Nothing is but thinking makes it so.

The Sceptical Witness

Chapter Ten: Red Herrings and Jigsaws

All my early years in forensic science seem to have been spent on a judicial helter skelter. Laboratory examinations were interspersed with a medley of court appearances, scene of crime searches and assistance at post mortem examinations. Into each available gap in these "official" tasks, no matter how small, I squeezed a small period of research and experimentation. If I were asked which of these several occupations I preferred most, I would have to place my experimental work at the top of the list. Here you will recognise the voice of the frustrated research scientist. But "research" had no official standing in the laboratory and was viewed with suspicion as a waste of time by most laboratory staff. This was a far cry from the situation, many years later, when one British laboratory director insisted that a research element was necessary in the work of every case-reporting scientist. This was in order to produce a balanced expert. But this was emphatically not the attitude in the fifties and sixties.

I always considered attendance at post-mortem examinations to be my least favourite forensic occupation. Partly this was because such examinations seemed to me to be the antithesis of laboratory research, and productive of nothing publishable in the scientific press. Also they tended to occur at unsociable times and were often smelly. Bodies in war, or at the scenes of murders, were one thing. Bodies on the slab, sometimes in an advanced state of rot, were quite another. Nevertheless these autopsies, in cases of suspicious deaths, were often the key to the whole investigative process. So many accidental deaths or suicides masquerade as possible murders, and vice versa, that no adequate sudden death investigation can function without the forensic pathologist. But the pathologist does not work against a rigid background scale of discrete quantities such as the scientist so often does. The pathologist's expertise consists of his knowledge of previous post mortem examinations in the form of a carefully assessed mental store that correlates the results from each of these previous autopsies with his findings in his latest case. This "subjective" pattern of experience lies at the far end of the knowledge scale away from the mathematical aspects of the physical sciences. Because of this it sometimes leads to a mutual incomprehension between practitioners at opposite ends of the qualitative/quantitative spectrum. "Forensic pathology? Our cat could do that!" was the comment of one forensic statistician. The *idola quantitatis* has its worshippers in forensic science as much as in other branches of science, and the fact that scientists can often work against a rigidly scalar background sometimes generates a contempt for those who work in more "subjective" fields. Neither is this an attitude which contrasts scientists and non scientists only. It also is evident amongst the various grades of "exact" sciences. But, for the moment, back to the post mortem slab.

It was a common sight for me to see the investigating officer impatiently awaiting the results of an autopsy while, at the same time, being compelled by the rules of good investigation practice to launch an enquiry on the basis of an assumption of the worst possible scenario. The confirmation of foul play by the pathologist, after a meticulous autopsy, may take some time if the job is to be done properly. Yet during the autopsy relevant developments can be occurring elsewhere. The trouble with crime investigation is that things can change so quickly that a piece of evidence available at one moment can disappear irrevocably should there be any delay in locating it. A suspect or a witness may vanish beyond the ken of the investigator, associated physical clues may be removed deliberately or damaged by the weather or other influences. Memories of events may fade or become corrupted by association with other, irrelevant, episodes.

So the essential requirement was that the forensic pathologist should make haste slowly in forming his conclusions. What was the cause of death? Were there injuries to the body? If so were these sufficient to cause death by themselves? Were the injuries caused by the deceased himself, by an attacker or by some other agency? Did any injuries present give a clue as to the nature of the instrument which caused them? When were the injuries caused? Was the victim found in the location where he died or was there evidence that the body had been moved after death? If there were no evident injuries to the body were there any signs of disease that could have caused death? Do the circumstances indicate that the death could have been caused by administration of a noxious substance? Were there any clinical indications that this might have been so? In cases where such possibilities occurred it was then the job of the pathologist to decide which relevant samples had to be taken from the body to be submitted for toxicological analysis at the laboratory.

My own function at post mortem examinations was to ensure that all necessary samples were taken which might be of value if the question of contact traces between the deceased and a suspect arose. Common among these samples were blood, vaginal and anal swabs, fingernail scrapings and surface fibres from the body, and I ensured the accuracy and continuity of this evidence by transporting it to the laboratory for my own, often lengthy, scientific examination. I never ceased to marvel at the cheerfulness of my forensic pathologist colleagues. Of the many I have met throughout my professional life not one can be said to have been of a morose nature. This is more than can be said for some of my legal, police and scientific colleagues, each profession possessing, in my experience, its equitable allotment of churlishness and gloom. Perhaps the reason that forensic pathologists are so buoyant is that forensic pathology is a job that is taken up only by a such characters. Or perhaps the temperament is generated by the job itself. The situation is, perhaps, analogous to the question "why do so many comedians come from Liverpool?" to which the reply is usually "one has to be a comedian to live there".

It was against such a background that my innate compulsion to see reason and pattern in natural phenomena was extended to trying to see the same properties in human institutions and behaviour. Here I was provided with a wonderfully rich field to work upon in the form of the judicial system of England and Wales. I was scientifically trained and I had little conception of the historical development of English legal institutions, looking at them through the eyes of a natural scientist. It took me some time to conclude that legal systems, like society itself, owed little of their structure to reasoning. During my long waits to give evidence in court I would often mentally design schemes to make the criminal trial swifter, fairer and more effective. The trouble was that I was largely unable to see how a system could be efficient if it had not been explicitly designed to be efficient by scientifically trained persons. How naive can one be? After a lifetime in the business I have come to the conclusion that the criminal lawyers have got it just about right. Not that they seem, over the centuries, to have been much concerned with logical design, or even with design at all. The system which has developed, the criminal trial in the common law countries, has grown organically and has evolved through experience. It has been subjected to the selection pressures of events and of changed human conditions and attitudes. In this way the criminal trial is analogous to the human body itself. Few scientists nowadays believe that the human body is a consequence of design; it is a product of a continuous process of natural selection. And so is the criminal trial. It is a creation not of logic but of experience.

The concerns of the criminal law start when it becomes evident that a crime has been committed. Thereafter the whole process, from the outset of the investigation to the end of the trial, can best be looked upon as a book of three chapters. The first chapter is the police investigation itself. This is a real time process in which the investigator reasons from effect (clue) to cause (the criminal) against a backdrop of change and decay in the evidence available. It is the investigator's aim to capture the evidence and to record it in an unchanging form while it is still available and uncorrupted. Classically this type of reasoning is called *a posteriori* reasoning. One considers a situation and tries to identify its cause. Chapter two in the story is a sort of mental buffer state. Here the investigator believes he has found the culprit and is in the process of designing the case that he is going to present to the court. He distils and refines the case, eliminating anything he considers irrelevant to the case against the person or persons he has charged with the offence. It is this mental model which is presented to the court in the form of accused person and charge. In a sense this is the end of the "whodunit?" stage of the process although, more often than not, evidence gathering does not stop at the moment an individual is charged with an offence.

Chapter Ten: Red Herrings and Jigsaws

Chapter three, the trial itself, considers the limited question of whether or not a named and charged individual did in fact commit the crime.

During the trial the type of reasoning used is in many ways the reverse of that used in the investigation. Here one is not concerned with "whodunit?" but with "did he do it?" Known classically as *a priori* reasoning, the court considers if a defined cause, an act committed by the defendant, could have given rise to the effects produced as evidence.

In the real world the two types of reasoning, *a posteriori* (effect to cause) and *a priori* (cause to effect), can seldom be separated. They alternate with each other in the mind in a network of mental cross checking which is always brought into play whenever a complex problem is being analysed. Nevertheless, for anyone concerned with crime investigation and the criminal trial, the distinction should be kept in mind because it highlights the differences between analysing the evidence from a crime on the one hand, and considering the case against an individual on the other.

In these technology-driven days few forensic scientists seem to find time for thinking about such basic matters. The mood is such that it is evident to practitioners, teachers and students that scientific laurels are bestowed for accomplishments which can be described in the form of algorithms, step by step explicit instructions, rather than for a general commentary on how one should think about problems in investigation. Such advice, so the current opinion holds, belongs to the nineteenth century rather than the twenty first. Whether anything can be done about the problem in the present climate of human thought is a moot point. In one long-running investigation (it had lasted several years) I happened to attend a case conference which had been called for the benefit of my paramount boss, the senior government official whose department included both police and forensic science. After listening to several hours of presentations we broke for a rest and he drew me into a corner and said with, I thought, a despairing edge to his voice "Kind, the police must be made to realise that crime investigation is a high grade intellectual pursuit"

The Sceptical Witness

I was dismayed. Not because of what he said (he was absolutely right) but because it was he who said it. Here was the most powerful man in the business, with over eighty thousand employees (not including police officers) in his department. If he couldn't do anything about it who could?

There is still great value for crime investigation in using thought patterns that have existed in public awareness for centuries. Although the advance of technology has given the crime investigator machine-assisted techniques which were not dreamed of forty years ago, it has also led to the widespread attitude that all advance in crime investigation is dependent upon the advance of technology and the production of "guidelines". Training people to think is more difficult than training them to operate machines. This does not imply that the operation of machines requires no judgement and attention, but the mental processes of the machine operator are grafted on to a set of operating instructions. Such mental activity does not have the free-roving nature which is common in connection with human actions and relationships.

Throughout my career I often heard the argument from colleagues that the ideal crime investigator would be a scientist and that he would act always in accord with scientific principles. Leaving aside the difficulty of defining the terms in such arguments I sometimes put forward the view that, other things being equal (which of course they seldom are) a historian would do a better job in crime investigation than a scientist. Such a view was seldom received sympathetically by those for whom "progress" was synonymous with "technological advance". Rudyard Kipling seems to have encapsulated much of the equipment of the good crime investigator when he wrote:

I keep six honest serving men
(They taught me all I knew)
Their names are What and Why and When
And How and Where and Who

although, for our purpose, it would be better for the serving men to appear in the order: *What?, Where?, When?, How?, Why?, Who?*.

The "what?" is the "it" of the "whodunit?" and thereafter the whole objective is to produce a solution for the "who?" So the kernel of the investigation is the "whodunit?" element. This is surrounded by elements of "wheredunit?", "whendunit?", "howdunit?" and "whydunit?". Each of these questions should be considered when weighing means, motive, opportunity, timing, location and modus operandi. Also to be kept in mind is the fact that words are simply an imperfect attempt by man to encapsulate a part of an infinitely variable universe, and that they connote attitude just as much as they connote events. In other words do not expect to be able to produce a set of explicit rules for dealing with complex and imponderable matters in the same way that a scientist may seek to formulate algorithms for his laboratory procedures. This is not to say that there are no circumstances in which it is useful to promulgate rules. Precept can be very useful as an *aide memoire* in a complex situation but the plea that one has followed the rules and the guidelines must not be used as an argument that responsibility for failure lies elsewhere. The only precepts worth having in crime investigation, apart from those dictated by law and the requirements of civilised behaviour, are those which facilitate and illuminate progress. No rules must be employed which can be used as props for the incompetent.

Crime investigation is analogous to piecing together a jigsaw puzzle without the assistance of the picture on the box lid. The criminal trial is more akin to being presented with a jigsaw puzzle together with the box lid picture. The picture will remain forever incomplete, at least in detail, but the investigator has the task of distilling his case against an individual from the limited number of pieces that is available. On the other hand the trial itself is more akin to being presented with a picture of a partially complete jigsaw picture by the prosecution. This partial picture consists of the accused, the act and the charge and these are followed up by the individual pieces of evidence to flesh out the prosecution case.

The Sceptical Witness

Strictly speaking, it is not the function of the criminal court to establish the truth, whatever that may be, of an event. Its job is the more
limited one of deciding if the evidence presented by the prosecution
to the court is sufficient to conclude that the accused person is guilty
of a specific charge. Neither is it job of the court to decide between the
states of guilt and innocence. Its job is to produce a verdict of "guilty"
(the evidence is adequate to support the charge) or of "not guilty" (the
evidence is inadequate to support the charge). One always hopes that
the verdict will reflect the true state of affairs but this is by no means
always so. As one English High Court judge once commented "'not
guilty' does not necessarily mean 'innocent'". It may be retorted that
neither does "guilty" necessarily mean "culpable", but one must always keep in mind that "guilty" verdicts should be "beyond reasonable
doubt". Herein lies the essence of the matter. A "not guilty" verdict is
simply a declaration that the prosecution has failed to establish its
case. It is, in modern digital jargon, a default decision. But, legally and
semantically fascinating though such considerations may be, we must
return to the practical world of the criminal trial.

The defence in a criminal trial is not compelled to produce its own
explanation of the evidence which is presented by the prosecution,
although it may be to its advantage to do so. It may just seek to show
that the prosecution evidence is faulty, false or inadequate. Many a
criminal case has been dismissed before the defence has produced any
evidence at all. The idea current amongst statistical writers that the
defence must produce an "alternative hypothesis", a sort of case for
innocence to oppose the case for guilt produced by the prosecution, is
a fallacy. It is a judicial red herring. It is a red herring that has its
origins in the classroom and the laboratory rather than in the courthouse. The roots of the fallacy spring from the world of the scientific
researcher where the problem is to produce causal explanations for
physical phenomena, usually on the borders of scientific knowledge.
Here the scientist must consider competing explanations for the events
he observes in order to produce the most likely explanation of the
occurrences which face him. This situation is exactly analogous to the
task of the crime investigator in that one considers effects in order to

identify causes. But once the case gets to court the situation changes. The charge encapsulates the investigator's belief that he has found the explanation, the cause, the criminal. The trial is not a "whodunit?". It is a "did-he-do-it"? It is the test of a belief. It is the analysis of the opinion of the investigator that he has solved the case and identified the culprit. The charge is a distillate made from events through information, evidence and indictment in that order. It is the mushroom on the compost heap. Civilised society must act against the transgressors against its laws and this it does through its criminal courts. It must decide if an accused person is guilty or not and, if the former, what to do about it. That is why the criminal court verdict is an operational decision. The court cannot allow itself the luxury of the unlimited debate enjoyed by research scientists. It tries a single issue, the charge against the accused and the court's decision is both exclusive and exhaustive, "guilty" or "not guilty". Although an alternative explanation is not a *sine qua non* of the defence in a criminal trial I was early impressed by the ingenuity of some defendants in producing these. Chapter 13, Coincidence and Paradigm, gives some ingenious examples. But for the moment let us return to the scene of the crime.

In the early years of my service provincial murder investigations were often directed by Scotland Yard officers sent up from London for specific cases. This usually happened when a small borough or county police force was involved. Such forces did not have the expertise necessary for a full scale murder investigation, and a chief constable who decided to go it alone without the assistance of the Yard ran the risk of adverse criticism. The involvement of the experienced London officers was, for the local force, an insurance against failure and, in those cases with a successful outcome, the Londoners usually had the sense to give the lion's share of the credit to the local CID. I was involved in perhaps a dozen murder cases with Scotland Yard officers over my first fifteen years service as a forensic scientist. My impression generally was of a professionalism which did not exist in many small provincial forces. Furthermore the Yard officers involved in a case usually had a substantial record in murder investigation of a depth unobtainable in a small organisation. If one wishes to do a job well one should do it frequently. This the Scotland Yard officers did. Not that things always worked out well, at least initially.

In one murder case the victim had been dislodged from his motor bike before being badly beaten and finally strangled with his own belt. All this was pretty evident from an initial examination of the scene. The badly bruised body lay on a grass surface which bore the scars of a desperate struggle. The ligature was still knotted around the neck of the deceased and his motor cycle lay nearby. The scene of the killing was the entrance to a boarding kennels that was run by the deceased and his wife, with the aid of an assistant. Scotland Yard was not called in immediately but when, after two or three days, it appeared that the investigation was not progressing well, a belated request was made to the Metropolitan Police for assistance. Soon thereafter two officers arrived to take over the investigation. By that time it appeared that the wife of the deceased and the assistant could be safely eliminated from suspicion because each had a watertight alibi. It is worth noting at this point that murder victims are more often killed by people they know than by strangers. This explains why relations and acquaintances must, at least initially, be members of the frame of suspects. In this case there were no other immediately evident suspects.

The body of the deceased lay on the frontage of his own property which was approached by a single narrow lane bordered by scrub trees. His movements were checked and it became evident that he was killed when he returned from the pub late in the evening after his habitual night's drinking there. A plausible theory was put forward that the deceased had been dislodged from his motorcycle by a trip wire at chest height strung between the trees bordering the narrow lane. This idea was proposed simply because it appeared to be the logical thing for a potential killer to do. To test this notion I, together with several police officers, checked along about fifty yards of lane to see if we could find any remnants of a trip wire. This we failed to do. The only wire we located was a burnt coil of copper wire on the residue of a bonfire amongst other miscellaneous rubbish. This was inside the kennels property itself.

Chapter Ten: Red Herrings and Jigsaws

On the arrival of the two Scotland Yard officers they examined the scene and questioned the wife and assistant. They agreed that the two could be eliminated, at least provisionally, from the enquiries and the investigation moved into new channels. After several weeks of hard work the killer was apprehended and interrogated. He made a full confession. It proved that he had been contracted by the wife to kill her husband. This was done with the connivance of the assistant, who was her lover. When the killer was asked how he had dislodged the victim from his motorcycle he replied that he had used a trip wire. Back at the scene he indicated where he had tied the wire. He then pointed out a fragment of the wire which remained attached to the tree after being broken by the impact of the motor cycle.

What a failure this was on our part. Both I and several police officers had already searched for such a trace of the act and we knew exactly what we were looking for. Then the Scotland Yard officers had done the same. Certainly the search was a lengthy and tedious one but it was necessary and had been done by experienced people. Yet it miscarried.

And what of the coil of wire on the bonfire? Now it appeared to be a major part of the evidence. The insulation, and any transfer traces, had been burned away in the fire but it was copper wire of the same gauge as the residual insulated fragment which remained attached to the tree. Had this remaining fragment of trip wire been located, when it should have been, then the picture would have all come together as an inside job. Thereafter the investigation would have been concentrated on the wife and her lover despite their well established alibis. Taking the reasoning a little further why was not more significance ascribed to the coil of burnt wire even in the absence of knowledge of the trip wire remnants on the tree? Should we not have viewed the burnt coil of wire with great suspicion, seeing it as the result of an attempt to destroy evidence? All this is obvious with the benefit of hindsight but at the time it was evident to none of us, including the Scotland Yard officers, the local police, and myself.

The Sceptical Witness

The investigation was not a failure *in toto* because the killer was arrested and convicted, but that should have happened several weeks earlier. Hindsight is a great clarifier of enigmas. Things look very different when one is reasoning *a posteriori* (from effect to cause) during the investigation, from how they do when one is reasoning *a priori* (from cause to effect) after the event. In the latter case everything tends to fall into place in a logical pattern. All of which does not obscure the fact that we early made a hash of the investigation and only redeemed ourselves later.

Some of the most enjoyable experiences of my career were when I met, years later, police officers with whom I had worked early on. Some of these had deservedly reached high rank. A chance meeting with one of them will serve to illustrate how foreknowledge, prejudice, *a priori* reasoning, call it what you will, may colour the decisions of an observer. At the time of the incident I am about to describe I was director of a laboratory in Berkshire in the south of England. There I met the Assistant Chief Constable of a southern police force whom I had known many years previously when he was a detective constable in Yorkshire. We discussed old times and old cases together, and we made arrangements to continue our discussions during a game of golf.

We met as arranged and completed the first hole which remarkably, considering my lack of ability at the game, I won. I drove off from the second tee and waited for my companion to do the same only to find that he had disappeared behind an adjacent bush to relieve himself. He shortly reappeared but, instead of proceeding with the game, he gripped me tightly by the arm and near dragged me back towards the clubhouse. I protested but was brusquely told that explanations would come later. Part way he abruptly stopped, took a bright red sweater from his golf bag, put it on and then continued hustling me towards the club house. Arriving there he speedily changed his shoes, urged me to do the same equally quickly, and then we got into his car and drove off. After a few miles we stopped at a pub for a drink and he gave me the explanation of his conduct. Readers may wish to try to identify the cause of his strange behaviour before reading further. He gave his explanation as follows. On going behind the bush and preparing to urinate he had been disturbed by an elderly lady who was taking her dog for a walk. He immediately rejoined me on the second tee and insisted we left, in case the lady made a complaint of indecent exposure.

I was amazed and told him so. There were, as I pointed out, thousands of such incidents every day on golf courses and other open spaces so why should he worry? There was absolutely no evidence which could be produced of indecent behaviour. He admitted that all this was correct but said that, when a senior police officer was the suspect for such an offence, evidence was unnecessary. A complaint in itself was sufficient. Were an allegation of indecency to be made against him, then he could expect no further professional advancement. Evidence of intent was unnecessary.

The act of exposure, and the complaint by the elderly lady, was all that would be required irrespective of the surrounding circumstances. There would be no tribunal of fact to consider the evidence. The slightest suspicion that he might have been involved in indecent behaviour would ruin any further chances of promotion in a highly competitive police world. Why should authority take a chance with someone who might be suspect when there were so many candidates without such clouds hanging over them?

In the event he heard no more about the matter and went on to even higher rank. But readers should ponder over this story both in terms of the reasoning processes of observers, and in terms of their own conceptions of "Justice".

And the detail of the red sweater?

I will leave you to work that out for yourselves.

The Sceptical Witness

Chapter Eleven: Miss Bailey's Ghost

In 1954, after two years in Wakefield, the laboratory moved to the town of Harrogate on the northern border of the West Riding. A greater difference from the commercial architecture of the southern half of Yorkshire would be hard to imagine. The factories and mills of the south were supplanted by the handsome town houses built by the prosperous merchants of the industrial West Riding. It was in this way that the rugged Victorian and Edwardian individualists had enjoyed the fruits of their labours at a safe distance away from the squalor created by their enterprises. Operating under the rubric "where there's muck there's brass" they left the muck in Leeds and Bradford and took the brass to Harrogate where they used it to build themselves fine mansions. I was rather pleased they had done so. Long dead, they had left the harvest of their ventures to be inherited by others, such as the staff of our own small laboratory. They could hardly have imagined the change to which one particular house was to be put. Any compassion I might have felt for my fellow humans, the misused workers who had made it all possible by their own poor living conditions, was somewhat blunted by a profound pleasure at being in such a congenial place

It was into one of the elegant villas that our laboratory moved and here I inherited the gem of the edifice, the master bedroom. Into this relatively huge apartment I installed my modest biology group. I positioned my desk at one end of the hall-sized room in a spot where I could see the distant Pennine hills through the window, dominated by the rounded massif of Blubberhouses Moor. The view was even better if I went out on to my own private balcony.

In these relatively luxurious conditions I designed and caused to be installed two enormous search tables topped with tough white plastic sheeting. These were to be used mainly for the searching of clothing and other large objects in the pursuit of evidence of crimes of violence. The tables had not been won without some differences of opinion with the director. He seemed to think that something the size of a card table would be quite adequate. But the success of applied science rests upon the design of furniture just as much as it does upon the products of laboratory research and I determinedly held out for my giant search tables. "Searching through a keyhole" was definitely not to my taste.

It was here that thirteen productive and fascinating years passed by. At the time we were the busiest laboratory in the United Kingdom in terms of throughput of casework although, after a while, we were overtaken by another laboratory which had a substantially larger staff and catchment area. But we still considered ourselves to be the leaders in forensic science, modest in size though we were. Looking back it is evident that it was at Harrogate that the seeds of the research ethos in forensic science were sown. We provided the lead and the rest of the country, and the world, followed.

It was in this laboratory that my realisation of the supreme importance of language blossomed. Until then I had been so busy learning the technical elements of my job that the communication and reporting aspects were relatively neglected. But not only did I have to labour at the scene-of-crime and in the laboratory but I had finally to express the results of my investigations in a written form. These statements had to be comprehensible to policemen, lawyers and to juries made up from the general public. The information in my reports had to be phrased in as balanced a manner as possible because, although I was nearly always called by the prosecution, in court I considered myself to be totally independent of both prosecution and defence. Not that this was always accepted by others involved in the criminal trial process and I sometimes exacerbated a naturally brusque manner with a somewhat ferocious independence. I had long ceased to be intimidated by wigs, gowns and court procedure and, if there were a particularly domineering counsel or irascible judge, I would mentally equalise the situation when I was in the witness box by imagining them naked, except for their wigs. It was not a pretty picture but by then I had a strong stomach.

Judges and counsel I found for the most part to be reasonable, balanced people although, as in all professions, there was the usual pro-

Chapter Eleven: Miss Bailey's Ghost

portion of journeymen and incompetents, a rust upon the machinery of justice. The interrupting judge and the unprepared counsel were the worst examples. Several times I have seen counsel, usually on a Monday morning, opening his case with his eyes stuck fast to his brief as he attempted to extract enough information from it, as he spoke, to convince the court that he knew what he was talking about. Then there was the dread of the bar, Mr Justice H..., who in one case, as was revealed on appeal, had spoken more words than the prosecution and defence counsel combined. But these were the exceptions and I soon began to appreciate the competence and compassion of most of the legal professionals as they tried to distil the essence of the evidence into a form which would allow the jury to make a reasonable decision. The more experienced I became the more I realised that I could not apply the attitudes appropriate to laboratory research to the discovery process of the criminal trial, much as I would have liked to have done so.

Although usually called by the prosecution, occasionally I was called by the defence. More often, if my report showed nothing of assistance to the prosecution, I would still be called by the prosecution who would then "tender" me to the defence. That is to say I would enter the witness box as a prosecution witness but would only be questioned by the defending counsel. This suited my conception of myself as an independent testifier. The same attitude was held by most, but not all, of my colleagues. The term "prosecution minded" was occasionally used of a minority of forensic scientists. On occasion I felt the title appropriate but in this matter, as in most affairs of judgement, truth has many aspects. One of my assistants at the time had a particularly malicious sense of humour and he used to wait for my return from court and artfully pose the question "did you get a conviction?" Subsequently I managed to get him transferred as assistant to a colleague of a less demanding nature than myself.

The Sceptical Witness

In one case I gave evidence for the prosecution when the defending counsel in cross examination asked me:

"Mr Kind, you appear as a witness for the prosecution. Can you convince the court that you are totally unbiased in this matter?" I replied "Well, I don't know if I'm unbiased. I certainly try to be".

And that of course, is the most any specialist witness can say and try to do. I realised that anyone might have an unconscious bias in the way he views "scientific facts" without even knowing it himself. We look upon the world from our own unique standpoint and we are expected to strip away all aspects of personal bias from that point of view before we express the result in such a way that others will grasp what is happening inside our minds. It is a frightening task under any circumstances, the more so if we don't make every effort to be understood. Unhappily few people realise the magnitude of the task of communication and we blithely undertake it, unconsidered, every day, whence comes misunderstanding. Bias, judgement, prejudice, experience, knowledge, learning, discrimination are all overlapping concepts and we are influenced by them according to our nature, origins, education and personal tastes. Each individual, including each forensic scientist, has a unique outlook on the world, even if only in detail.

This was brought home to me again many years after the transfer of our laboratory to Harrogate. In the eighties and nineties a profound change took place in the organisation of forensic science in Britain when many of my erstwhile colleagues moved across from government into the private sector. All of those I have spoken to since their moves have been astonished how new perspectives on the production of scientific evidence in the criminal trial have been opened to them. And this, remember, is the experience of highly seasoned forensic practitioners. But, back in the fifties, I had great difficulty even communicating with forensic scientist colleagues who were doing the same type of work as I, in other regions of England and Wales. The horizon of the forensic scientist in the fifties was largely limited to colleagues in his own laboratory. Yet it had become evident to me after a short time in the job that communication with other forensic scientists was a basic necessity for improvements in forensic science practice. We learned by our mistakes but it would have been far more effective to learn, in addition, by the mistakes our colleagues had already made. But contact with the six other laboratories in the country was virtually non-existent. True, the seven laboratory directors occasionally held meetings together but there was seldom a full roll call of participants and we never learned what they discussed.

The problem was that most of the directors were former academics who viewed each other with the deepest possible suspicion. Each was determined to keep each his own laboratory as a little kingdom independent of the others. The government administrators who were responsible for the overall structure of the forensic science laboratories (it wasn't called a "service" then) must have despaired of their scientists. The senior administrators, "mandarins" as we tended to call them, were always in my experience supportive of interchange of experience and mature discussion but they had met their reactionary match in a group of stubborn academics.

I tried to convince my own director that meetings with the staff of other laboratories could only lead to improvements in our practices but he seemed to be of the view that I should know it all already and, if I didn't, I should pick it up from books. My frustration lasted for several years during which time I tried to stimulate the interest in, and the means to, a regular system of communication amongst forensic scientists. I raised little interest in the laboratory mainly, I think, because my colleagues were so busy doing case work that they had little time to think about other matters. Furthermore few people thought that sufficient interest could be stimulated amongst the few forensic scientists existing at that time for regular organised meetings to take place.

Finally I gave up trying to convince people and I set up a one-man society myself. I called it the *Society for Forensic Science* and I ran it from my kitchen table. Viewed by most of my colleagues with quiet amusement or with incredulity it infuriated the laboratory director. He hinted at grave obstacles to the development of my career should I persist in my actions. I persisted. In truth I could hardly do anything useful with such a society without both finance and wide support so I concentrated on organising a meeting to set up a more formal association. Finally I gained the moral support of one of my colleagues in the laboratory who also agreed to pay half of the not inconsiderable cost of an advertisement in the main British scientific publication *Nature*.

In this advertisement we formally announced our intention to set up an academic society to deal with the subject of forensic science. Then things began to move. A colleague from another laboratory joined our small group and, wonder of wonders, persuaded his own director to enrol in our growing band. My delight at this event was sharpened by the knowledge that the director concerned, and my own, enjoyed an acute and mutual loathing. Few organisational decisions are taken in the absence of such human aspects. Neither are such events entirely free from of an element of malicious enjoyment such I experienced here.

The next step was to decide where the foundation meeting of the new society should take place. I was determined that it would not be in London. I felt that, should it do so, it would fall under the influence of the established London medicolegal societies and become local, with only a derisory provincial membership. Or perhaps it would just evolve into a sort of livery guild, an organisation which, bearing the name of a useful art, functions largely on the charitable and social scene. The capital city of any country tends to act as a sort of black hole for intellectually based organisations and it would have been difficult, once established there, for the gravitational pull of a London base to be resisted. The larger part of the population, that which lives in the provinces, tends to be regarded as a secondary feature of intellectual life. "Provincial malcontents" was one term I heard used in this connection. So I went ahead and called the meeting on my own erstwhile ground in Nottingham University. Hoping for the support of the staff of the long established and highly respected Nottingham Forensic Science Laboratory I then wrote to a colleague there and requested his assistance. His reply was distinctly pessimistic. It appeared that the members of the laboratory staff there thought that the idea of a forensic science society had little to commend it and that it would certainly fail through lack of support. Furthermore because they did not intend to be an element in my failure they would not take part. I kept this letter for a long time and when, years later, its writer became vice president of the now large and successful Forensic Science Society I took pleasure in showing it to him. A humorous and kindly man he roared with laughter at my mischievous pleasure.

My last step in organising the foundation meeting was to ask a friend, an academic with no forensic science connections, to take the chair at the gathering. I did this because I knew he was a good meetings chairman and I also wished to avoid charges of favouritism to any particular laboratory, or to any forensic specialism, by appointing a forensic scientist.

The meeting was a great success and, in October, 1959, The Forensic Science Society came into being. Since then it has never looked back, except with pride, at its achievements. From the beginning it has been a "broad church" society of legal, police, medical and scientific professionals. The story of the Forensic Science Society would take an entire book to tell and it is not my intention to try to tell it here except for one aspect.

This aspect starts at the foundation meeting when, after the constitution had been approved and most of the officers had been appointed, difficulty was experienced in finding an editor. I had never done any editing before but finally, *faute de mieux*, the job fell to me. It lasted for fifteen years. For most of that time The *Journal of the Forensic Science Society* was produced on that same kitchen table upon which the foundation meeting was organised. Together with my wife, Evelyn, we acted as unpaid editors, sub editors, proof readers and everything else that is associated with the publication of a learned journal. Everything that is with the exception of printing it. That fell to the local newspaper printing firm in Harrogate. There the staff willingly turned from their main task of producing newspapers and bus timetables to become scientific printers. Happily they proved more than equal to the job.

So my life became even busier. I had a hectic full time job and now I had the task of producing a scientific journal twice yearly. Twice yearly soon became quarterly and the Journal became a major component in my life and that of my family. Because the staff were unpaid the Journal made a profit right from its inception and this contributed to the development and stability of the Society. Being editor also put me in the line of literary fire. Although most scientists are reluctant authors they share with many other readers the pleasure in pointing out when the editor splits his infinitives or dangles his participles. Not having received a literary education, splittings and danglings were probably more frequent than they should have been. But that is the consequence of the founder members appointing me on a *faute de mieux* basis.

It was the Journal which stimulated and maintained my interest in language but I sometimes despaired of trying to read sense into some of the typescripts which were sent to me for publication. The trouble is that although the meaning of a text is always clear to its own author it is difficult to convince him that it will not be equally clear to others when they try to read it. I found that some scientific authors were surprisingly lofty in their attitudes towards editors. A request for an author to clarify his text could be met with an implication that perhaps the shortcomings were entirely on the editor's side. After all, communication is a two party affair and one could hardly expect an editor to understand such important and highly expert material. But the editor could rest assured that those specialists to whom the article was addressed would be able to understand it.

Such attitudes received short shrift from me. Having received neither the benefit of a classical education in literature, nor of a finishing school in manners, I was occasionally moved to suggest that publication was perhaps not the most profitable end use for an author's typescript. Not surprisingly the all-consuming desire of most authors to see their name in print usually led to a softening of approach. Thereafter the acceptance of reasonable alterations led to publication. On a very few occasions, wonder of wonders, it also led to the admission that the published text was very much better than the original script.

Language develops swiftly in the world of science. Fresh words are coined to describe recently discovered facts or newly proposed theories. These words are often manufactured from Greek or Latin roots. But once coined, a word can drift in meaning in exactly the same way that everyday words do and it can take on a specialist meaning that the original coiner did not intend. One such example that I commented upon in a rather despairing editorial was "artefact". This word, defined in the dictionaries as meaning "artificial product", is one that has been adopted by scientists to describe the irrelevant consequences which are generated by defects in the design of an experiment. It describes the unwanted trimmings, the irrelevant garnish, which sometimes obscures the clarity of an experimental result.

In this sense the word is a development of the original meaning of "artificial product". Of course one might argue that all experiments are artefacts in their entirety but it would have been pointless to do so because the word is so well established in its scientific use. It is in this drifting way that new words and meanings come into use and evolve even to the point of becoming a new language. After all, that is how French, Italian and Spanish were formed from vulgar Latin in the debris of the Roman empire. But the change in the meaning of a word must not take place so swiftly that a listener or reader cannot grasp what it means.

This drift in the meaning of words is something that many people find hard to accept. The view that a word means what the speaker or writer intends it to mean, or what the listener or reader comprehends it to mean, irrespective of what the dictionary says, is one which has many enemies. A colleague who once expressed this point of view on a radio programme subsequently received a flood of hate mail. One of these letters informed him bluntly that he was just the sort of individual who allowed his dog to foul the pavement. Thus does language raise hackles.

In one of the scripts I received I noticed that the meaning of "artefact" had developed even further and was used by the author to describe misleading signs in a non-experimental situation. The case in question was one where a burned body had been found at the scene of a fire and the author drew attention to a particular effect of the fire on the body which might make an unwary pathologist draw the wrong conclusions during a post mortem examination.

Even more confusing than the drift of meaning in words is the case of the author who jauntily makes up new words as he goes along. William Shakespeare was adept at this and his coinings, in many cases, are still active in modern usage. What were "neologisms" in Shakespeare's day (if the word existed then) are now highly valued building bricks in the English language. But what Shakespeare did in his plays is not to be recommended in a scientific paper. In one long article that I refereed for publication I noted nearly thirty neologisms, words made up by the author and not yet in any dictionary. In no case did he think it necessary to define what he meant by his newly minted word. Presumably he didn't know he was minting them.

But apart from avoiding private meanings another requirement is for the author to keep his scientific text as short as possible consistent with making his meaning clear. Scientific writing is not creative writing, it is expository writing. The importance of good expository writing is nowadays formally recognised by most higher education organisations. Years after my service as editor I was delighted to learn that some of my writings had been adopted as examples of good style by the "School of Expository Writing" of a major American university. I can only hope that the present reader is of the same view. If not, please don't write.

Chapter Eleven: Miss Bailey's Ghost

My preferred example of a good condensed text is the first verse of an early nineteenth century English broadside ballad. If the purpose of language is to express oneself both efficiently and economically, it would be hard to better:

A Captain Bold in Halifax
Who dwelt in country quarters
Seduced a maid who hanged herself
One Monday in her garters.

These twenty one words give the man's profession, character, residence, and what he did. They refer to the marital status of the girl, what she did, how and when she did it and, by implication, why. As Jeremy Bentham said "The more words there are, the more words there are about which doubts may be entertained".

I remember being most impressed early on in my career when I received my first subpoena to attend an Assize Court. Couched in rather archaic language it enjoined me to attend "... all business set aside and all excuses ceasing." I wonder if the modern subpoena exists in an "improved" version designed to aid comprehension? The old one has always seemed pretty crystalline to me.

For me the most impressive example of how ambiguity of words can influence the reasoning of a court lies in a story told to me by my first laboratory director. It was of an inquest in a large provincial city in England during the nineteen thirties. The purpose of the inquest was to determine the cause of death of a patient who died on the operating table when an explosion occurred. There was no doubt that the material which exploded was diethyl ether, commonly referred to simply as "ether" - the anaesthetic in use at the time. The problem was to decide how this very volatile and flammable substance had been ignited. There were no naked flames present, neither did it seem possible that an electrical spark had been responsible for the ignition because there was no electrical apparatus adjacent to the site of the explosion. None of the evidence shed any light on the cause of the explosion.

The Sceptical Witness

A verdict of "accidental death" was returned to which the coroner added his own theory as to the cause of the ignition. Pointing out that, shortly before the accident, a new radio transmitting station had been established near the hospital, the coroner observed that the ignition had occurred because it was well known that "radio waves pass through the ether". This was a confusion of two different words, each spelt the same way but with different meanings. These word pairs occur commonly enough to warrant their own special name. They are called "homonyms". The coroner had confused "ether", an actual chemical substance, with "ether", a hypothetical medium invented by scientists to account for the properties of radio waves. Subsequently I told this story many times in police and forensic science circles and it was always received with great amusement. However with the passage of time I became more sceptical of the "obvious" view of decision making and, in thinking about this case, I later concluded that the coroner might well have been right, even if for the wrong reason.

Radio transmitters can, in fact, generate accidental sparks in nearby objects, particularly metal ones. If the metal is corroded this tends to increase the danger of sparking. What happens is that a corroded junction between two metal surfaces can act as a "rectifier" of radio waves causing a large voltage to build up across the corroded boundary. Above a certain voltage, dependent upon conditions, this can lead to a tiny, but extremely hot, electrical spark which can easily ignite flammable gases. Before the war plastics technology was fairly primitive compared with today and a higher proportion of metal was used in medical and scientific apparatus. Because corrosion prevention was much less effective in those days then this could have led to the production of instruments which were more prone to sparking in a radiofrequency field than would be modern apparatus. So perhaps, as the coroner said, the patient died because radio waves passed through the ether.

Verbal misconceptions can last for many years and be copied from one written record to another. I was early puzzled by a statement repeated by several fingerprint authors who asserted that the individual nature of fingerprints had been known in biblical times. This was based upon the phrase:

"..he seals up the hand of every man, that all men shall know his work" (Job 37,7).

Fascinated by the subject of personal identity I had long interested myself in the individual nature of fingerprints and had read widely on the subject. Nothing that I had read convinced me that there was anything published before the middle of the nineteenth century that provided compulsive evidence that the personal nature of fingerprints had been known before that time. Granted that anyone with good eyesight, intelligence and an enquiring mind might have concluded that fingerprints were peculiar to the individual. I sometimes think that the ancient Greeks might have been interested in the subject. It is at least possible that Plato looked at the tips of his fingers as he was ruminating on the question of Platonic "Forms". It is also at least possible that some reflective shepherd, amongst the millions of reflective shepherds in human history, whiled away his time in the summer hills by musing on the individuality of the diminutive loops and whorls at the end of his fingers. They were obvious to his sharp eye, much easier to observe than his navel, and there was nothing else to do while his mere presence deterred the attentions of unwelcome predators from his sheep.

Furthermore the Chinese seem to infer from time to time that the individual nature of fingerprints has been known to them from long ago. The support for that claim is both amplified and obscured by the nature of the Chinese written language. Reading written Chinese is more a question of describing pictures than of construing declarations. Meaning in such circumstances can easily become lost in a surfeit of interpretation. But whatever the truth of the matter it seemed to me that the biblical phrase "...he seals up the hand of every man..." was scanty evidence that fingerprints were implied by the biblical author. Consider the ambiguity of the verb "to seal" in the English language. It can imply the imposing of a distinctive identity on an object ("signed and sealed") or it can denote that the object has been securely fastened up. In practice it can mean a combination of the two meanings.

So I went to the French and Spanish language bibles and I found that the verb used in each language simply meant "to disable". Next, following the scientist's commonly repeated injunction to refer to original sources, I asked a forensic scientist in Jerusalem to tell me what the Hebrew version implied. Once again the answer was "disable". So the word "seal", as used in the biblical quotation, has nothing to do with the concept of individuality. But there is no doubt that uncritical writers will continue to use it as evidence that the individuality of fingerprints was known in biblical times. *Caveat lector*, let the reader beware. Assertions become hallowed by publication.

But not only assertions become hallowed, so do inadvertent errors. Sometimes such slips even survive to become part of a language, at least for a time. During my wartime aircrew training one printed training circular told the story of the instructor who was teaching skip bombing techniques. This method of assaulting the enemy's shipping required a low flying aircraft to released its bomb just before reaching the target. The theory was that with the low altitude of release, and the aircraft's speed, the bomb would bounce from the surface of the water and penetrate into the side of the ship. Throughout his lesson the instructor used the verb "to sofle" to describe the action of the attacking aircraft. It was only when one of his students checked the written instructions on the method that he located the origin of the neologism. There was a proof reading error. A phrase which should have read "..........and so fling the bomb at the ship......" was lacking a space between two words, producing the apparent participle "sofling" and, by extension, the verb "to sofle"

Continuing the theme that words are dangerous objects to those who seek meaning, let us consider one of the most, or perhaps the most, ambiguous word in forensic science, the word "control". This is a word that was imported into English from French about five hundred years ago and since that time it has maintained its two original meanings of "direction" or "command" on the one hand and "check" or "verify" on the other. The first meaning is dominant in English and the second in French. Nevertheless it is in its secondary English meaning that it has been adopted into the language of science. Thus a "control sample" in an experiment is a check sample. Potentially then "control" is a very useful word. But a word is only of value to the extent that its users know what it means, and employ it in the same sense. However "control" has proved a powerful factor in the blunting of meaning in forensic science. It was intended to serve as a name for those elements in an experiment which were designed to ensure that irrelevant factors did not influence an experimental outcome. This was a perfectly reasonable importation into scientific language. But the use of the word in forensic science is a model of ambiguity and it is almost impossible to determine what the word means there. Originally a useful label in experimental situations, in forensic science it has now drifted into use as a label for substances and objects which are submitted to the laboratory.

In the field of physical evidence there are three classes of materials which must be considered by the forensic scientist when searching for transferred traces. These are (1) materials known to be associated with the crime, (2) materials suspected to be associated with the crime and (3) materials from reference sources used for exclusion or identification. The reader may care to ponder on this codification for a moment in relation to the various types of crime against persons or property.

Together with a group of colleagues I decided to investigate the occurrence of the word "control" in articles published in three major forensic science journals throughout a four year period. We found examples of the word "control" used to describe materials recovered from the scene of a crime, materials recovered from the person of a suspect, and materials kept in a laboratory reference collection as aids to identification. So what does the word mean in the forensic science context? Personally I have no idea, except in the experimental situation where, to me, it still means "check". The extension of the word to non-experimental situations has happened unnecessarily and illogically.

The Sceptical Witness

The wholesome desire to avoid sexual discrimination in the written word can also lead to a misleading text. In a recent survey of forensic science cases in the south west of England it would appear that all the persons involved in several dozen criminal cases were female. This included criminals, lawyers, scientists and police officers. But this was not a general survey, it purported to be a series of descriptions of actual cases. Is not this "gender distortion" (I've just invented the term) a deliberate misrepresentation of evidence, an example of linguistic terrorism? But I had best be careful and keep in mind the fate of the colleague mentioned earlier who made a radio broadcast on the subject of what words mean and so attracted a flood of hate mail. I would not wish, like him, to be accused of being the sort of person who allowed his (her) dog to foul the pavement. In such circumstances the fact that I don't own a dog would carry little evidential weight.

Science cannot depend upon the oral tradition, upon the shifting sands of the spoken word. It depends upon writing and publication. Scientists cannot maintain a consistent logical position without writing. A verbally expressed opinion can change with time without even the holder himself noticing the shift. An experimental observation, or a conceptual view, must be fixed in the record at a certain time for its maximum value to be exploited. On most occasions this means publication in the scientific press. But most forensic scientists are reluctant to write for publication. Perhaps this is a consequence of writing so much for the police and for the courts that it leaves little enthusiasm and energy for the preparation of articles. Even if the scientist overcomes the other demands on his time and goes to the extent of preparing an article for publication it still has to face the editor and the referees. The choice of referees, those who will advise the editor on whether or not to publish, is itself fraught with difficulties. The more specialised an article the more the editor must rely on his referees in his decision whether to publish or not. The more specialised the article, the smaller the group from which to choose a referee and the more likely it is that personal factors will intrude.

Chapter Eleven: Miss Bailey's Ghost

These and other factors made my formative years as an editor very difficult and I often thought I had bitten off more than I could chew. Discreet enquiries made it evident that there was no-one else available in those early years who would be willing and able to take on the job. If I gave up as editor then the Journal would fold and so would the Society. The "free" distribution of the Journal to members constituted the major attraction of Society membership at that time. But the input of manuscripts into the editorial in-tray was very slow even though I begged and bullied colleagues mercilessly to produce articles for me. In addition, as a civil servant, I was under the requirement that any of my own writings had to be approved by my department before publication. I blithely ignored this requirement until the publication of one of my editorials in which I described the English legal system as a "ramshackle machine". By now my superiors had had enough and they firmly pointed out that this assertion would not have been approved by them for publication. In future, they decreed, anything signed by me must be submitted to them for approval. So I stopped signing my editorials.

It wasn't long before I was in trouble again. This time I had written an editorial on alcohol and driving. Entitled *Driving over the level* it would be considered very ordinary stuff nowadays. It argued that a defined level of alcohol in the blood or urine should be taken as evidence of an offence committed by a drinking driver. The stumbling block to the adoption of such a law was that people had great difficulty separating, in their minds, the level of alcohol in the blood from its supposed effect on driving. So it was felt that the assumption that a certain alcohol level in the blood reflects unfitness to drive was unfair to those who could hold their liquor. But this was not the point. The point was, I felt, that legislation on blood alcohol level and driving should contain no presumption as to effect. It should be a blunt prescriptive level. Above that level one should be guilty of an offence and the offence should be simply that of being above that level. It would be a law analogous to the speed limit laws.

The Sceptical Witness

All this is dreadfully old fashioned to the modern reader but it was the subject of active debate at the time. On the day the editorial was published a bill on the subject was being argued in the House of Lords of the British parliament. Feeling that it was unlikely that many of their lordships were subscribers to my Journal, I sent a copy of the unsigned editorial to each of the active debaters. This I did despite the rule that civil servants should not attempt to influence politicians with their own individual opinions in such matters.

Retribution followed swiftly. I was called up to London and faced by a panel of three very senior persons. They were so senior in fact that each bore the title "Sir". I was asked why I had transgressed the rules and attempted to influence the decisions of politicians. I pointed out to them that the editorial was unsigned. They pointed out to me that, where an editorial was unsigned, it was reasonable to suppose that the editor had written it. The point was a powerful one and I had to concede. No story follows of how a martyr to a free press was victimised by his bosses. In fact the whole affair was genial and civilised and I was left with the feeling that my three knights had a powerful point. I remember discussing the matter with some of my colleagues on my return to the laboratory. Each commiserated or gloated according to his nature. All agreed I had committed a grave career error and that my future progress would be minimal. A few years later I was promoted, over the heads of people senior to myself, to be director of my own laboratory.

During a somewhat turbulent career I cannot remember feeling victimised at any time and it is a credit to the civil service department for which I worked that it was maintained as a broad church into which even "misfits" such as I fitted without too much difficulty. The senior administrators could hardly run a ship in which each crew member was allowed to go his own way and I was allowed a great deal of freedom. Thinking back it is evident that I received more antagonism from scientists than from the broadly educated arts man who ran the upper echelons of the job. It's a thought for my next time round perhaps.

Chapter Eleven: Miss Bailey's Ghost

Much later my career was finally brought to a close by my public opposition to the treatment of one of my forensic scientist colleagues in the department. This book is no place to write about such a sad affair and I doubt if I would be qualified to write a separate volume on the subject. Those involved in military actions seldom grasp the overall picture of the entire battle. Sufficient to say I thought the main player in the tragedy was very similar to the central character in *L'Etranger* by Albert Camus. This character, you may remember, was convicted of murder because he didn't cry at his mother's funeral. In a similar way my colleague was something of a distinctive individual and he sometimes appeared as though he would have fitted better into Victorian England than into the twentieth century. As such he never matched comfortably with his more flexible colleagues. Thus when the intermingling currents of developing events left him isolated, he found few supporters. My own opposition to his treatment culminated in a very public way. It took the form of a letter of protest sent to the Times newspaper of London. It was printed as the leading letter in the correspondence columns.

This was not the thing for a senior civil servant to do and I obviously had to go. My going was arranged in as civilised and courteous fashion as possible and at my own request. In exchange for volunteering to vacate the plum laboratory directorship of the service I was allowed into voluntary exile to take over the laboratory which serviced my adoptive county in the north of England. The serving director of that laboratory, a highly competent scientist, must have been amazed at the turn of events as he was abruptly exchanged with me for "career development reasons". But he went on to be a highly appreciated and popular figure in his unforeseen research job. He probably did far better in it than did his predecessor.

It was all done quietly and decently. The only venom that I received in the matter was from my immediate superior, a scientist. Eighteen months later, when the hullabaloo had died down, I took the opportunity quietly to retire. This I did by getting the department to agree to contract me to write a book on *The Scientific Investigation of Crime* and to publish the result. I wrote it and they didn't like it and refused to publish it. However they allowed me to publish a limited edition which soon sold out. Enquiries about the book continued to arrive and so, ten years later I wrote to my erstwhile department and asked their permission to publish a second edition. They did not trouble to reply. One can hardly blame them. They probably thought they'd already had enough of me, poor devils. Some time after I had retired a younger, still working, colleague from the service told me a story. He had been waiting for a management meeting to start when a senior civil service administrator slid into the next chair. The new arrival looked at my friend for a while then he said. "You're S... aren't you? Tell me S..., this chap Kind, have you cut him adrift yet"? It is, I suppose, a sad comment upon my character that I think of this story with as almost as much pleasure as when I think of my disciplinary meeting with the three noble knights.

I sometimes look back upon a series of vehement defences of what I saw as matters of high principle and conclude that, for all the effect it had, I may as well have avoided all the hassle. Human affairs have a habit of proceeding in their own inevitable way, independently of the minority who swim against the stream. Perhaps one of the important lessons to be learned from life is that it is neither cowardice nor failure to withdraw from lengthy disputes about principles. We all need to concern ourselves mainly with the commonplace demands and realities, and occasional joys, of everyday life. This we should learn early in life. Unfortunately I never did. Perhaps an appropriate epitaph would be the old doggerel:

Here lies the body of walker Jay
Who died defending his right of way
He was right, dead right, as he walked along
But he's just as dead as if he'd been wrong

Chapter Twelve: The Ladder of Expertise

During my years in Yorkshire our laboratory work increased as the police progressively realised that much of value in crime investigation and the criminal trial could result from the scientific examination of crime scenes and samples. But the government department responsible for our laboratory did not react immediately to our cries for more staff. So we spent our time in a chronically understaffed condition, or so we thought. But the positive side of what we considered to be a regrettable situation was that we compensated by seeking to improve the speed and efficiency of the examination methods we used. So we invented new techniques to solve old problems. In this way our small laboratory became a ferment of research, or at least it did for one of my colleagues and myself. I was mainly interested in the characterisation of human body fluids. He was mainly concerned with detecting poisons and drugs in human entrails and other organs. We were jokingly nicknamed "Blood" and "Guts" respectively. The research we did was often carried out in the evening because there was no time for it during the day.

One remarkable success which my colleague enjoyed was the first ever proof of a murder by insulin poisoning. This was a phenomenal attainment because of the demanding and laborious analytical methods of those days. He was a very determined and dedicated man and when he asked me to become involved in the case I demurred because of the amount of work involved. Just imagine, had I accepted I might have become famous by association. Years later "Guts" deservedly became the acknowledged world doyen of chemical toxicology. My own success was somewhat more modest. A generous helping of indolence, mixed with a tendency to day-dream, is a powerfully blunting influence on a will to succeed.

At the time we needed new methods to speed our work without sacrificing accuracy. To do this we had to concentrate on those routine examinations which took up most of our working time. Unlike academic research we could not first invent a problem to solve and then invent its solution. Our problems were thrust upon us by circumstances. Because of this I have always believed that applied research is more demanding than the pure variety.

The commonest problem I faced in routine work was the location and confirmation of semen stains on clothing. This type of information is often of use as evidence in cases of sexual assault. In those early years the usual way of locating such stains was to examine the clothing under ultraviolet light. Under this illumination, which is invisible in itself, the semen fluoresces a pale blue. It is not a bright fluorescence, and other common substances fluoresce similarly. So it was not a good test although it was better than nothing.

There was another factor too which lessened the value of the test. This was the increasing use of artificial brighteners in the manufacture and cleaning of clothing. These chemicals fluoresce brilliantly under ultraviolet light and they obscure the relatively modest fluorescence of the dried semen. So it often happened that the examination of fluorescent spots on clothing by microscopical methods failed to prove the presence of semen. On many occasions our attempts to confirm semen proved fruitless because we had been misled by an irrelevant fluorescence.

What was required was a method which would show precisely the location of the semen stains on clothing irrespective of what other stains were present. I finally solved this problem by producing a scheme which located a substance called acid phosphatase. This is an enzyme that occurs in large amounts in the fluid produced by the male gland, the prostate. Prostatic fluid mixes with other secretions to form male semen. If one searches for acid phosphatase, instead of for fluorescent substances, the test provides a far more specific indication of semen. Nevertheless, although a positive reaction in the test was highly suggestive of semen we always carried out a confirmatory examination. This took the form of a microscopical examination for spermatozoa. These are the tiny tadpole-like cells which carry half the genetic code to the female egg. The female egg carries the other half.

Chapter Twelve: The Ladder of Expertise

My scheme was simply to cover the article under inspection with a large damp sheet of white blotting paper. On this paper the outline of the garment was drawn. After leaving the paper in contact with the clothing for a few minutes, it was removed and placed on a white plastic topped bench. Next the paper was sprayed with a substance that caused any tiny traces of acid phosphatase that had been extracted to develop a bright red-blue colour. In this way any stains of semen on a garment could be visualised, panoramically, as bright coloured patches on the sheet of white blotting paper, rather like the detail on a coloured map.

It proved a very efficient method and, after a successful trial, I published an account of it in the *American Journal of Police Science* (this was several years before I established a separate British forensic science journal). The method improved our effectiveness in semen cases enormously and it was swiftly taken up by other laboratories. It also had the unforeseen effect of mystifying Her Majesty's Stationery Office. They demanded to know why the yearly consumption of blotting paper of one small forensic science laboratory equalled that of the entire Inland Revenue Department.

Another interesting consequence of the new method occurred when I invented some stable test papers for acid phosphatase. These required only the addition of water to make them active agents for acid phosphatase detection. This would be useful, I believed, for those laboratories which found it inconvenient to make up the, rather unstable, reagent in liquid form. Chatting with a police surgeon colleague at court one day I mentioned the test papers to him. He became interested in them and asked for a sample to try out. So I gave him a container with the test papers carefully stored over a drying agent. In this condition I had found that they remained useable for several months. Almost immediately semen detection cases stopped arriving from his police force. Subsequently he told me that he was now doing them himself with the aid of my papers. I gently convinced him that the papers, although excellent as a screening test, were not really enough to prove the presence of semen to the degree required by a court of law. There still remained the necessity for an expert microscopic examination for sperm, a technique that his small office and surgery was not equipped to do. He saw the point and the semen examination cases from his police force resumed their appearance at the laboratory. This is yet another example of a general rule. If one designs a new procedure to produce a desired effect, then the likelihood is that it will produce unforeseen and unwanted effects too. Perhaps this is just another example of Murphy's Law. I'm not sure.

When dealing with human tissues and body fluids the forensic scientist does not deal with pristine clinical samples produced under aseptic conditions in a doctor's surgery or a hospital. The materials examined by a forensic scientist are often unclean. In many cases they can only be described as filthy. Sometimes they are also decomposed. So the forensic scientist may be faced with the problem of cleaning up a sample before being able to analyse it. This problem was regularly encountered in the examination of bloodstains and, occasionally, in the examination of decayed flesh. This question sometimes arose when the police had the task of deciding if a particular bloodstain at the side of a road, or a piece of rotting flesh floating in a river, was the consequence of a criminal act. Usually such objects were not. The bloodstain was most often that of a sheep, a dog, a rabbit or a bird which had been killed by a motor vehicle. Likewise the piece of rotting flesh from a river was usually animal. Sheep seemed to drown fairly regularly and, when the flesh became detached from the wool, the rotting fragments sometimes took on a suspiciously "human" appearance. Then problems of identification arose.

The standard laboratory routine to identify such materials was to use the "precipitin test". In this test a specially prepared rabbit blood serum was placed in the bottom of a very small test tube. This liquid is transparent, viscous and slightly straw coloured. In it are factors known as "anti-human antibodies". To find out if a bloodstain, or piece of flesh, is of human origin a very dilute and clear extract is made of it and this is layered upon the top of the rabbit serum already in the tube. This extract is much more dilute than the rabbit serum and so it

Chapter Twelve: The Ladder of Expertise

shows no tendency to mix if layered carefully. If human blood is present then, after a few minutes, a white opalescent ring appears at the junction of the two liquids.

This description gives the essence of the test, and sufficient detail for our present purpose, although the actual analysis has many more safeguards built in. But the essential requirement is that both liquids must be clear in order for the opalescent ring to be seen, if it is there. This is no problem with the rabbit serum because it is a commercial product manufactured to specified standards. But with the sample under test it can be a different story. Sometimes an extract from a bloodstain or from flesh is so cloudy that it obscures any opalescent ring which might be present.

So I invented a method which plugged the tube with a transparent jelly just above the rabbit serum. Thereafter one could layer a turbid extract on the top of the jelly because the ring forming reaction was mediated by soluble factors from each liquid. These could easily diffuse into the jelly layer. But any turbidity in the sample would be kept away from the ring-forming region simply because the submicroscopic holes in the jelly are too small to allow turbidity particles through. It was a simple but effective method and it provided one more modest rung for me as I climbed the ladder of expertise.

But the greatest hindrance that I regularly encountered in laboratory examinations was the problem of grouping bloodstains. At the time of which I speak, the nineteen fifties, the only way of characterising human blood for forensic purposes was the determination of its ABO blood group. Granted there were other human blood groups which were known, and some were occasionally applied in forensic work, but the results could be ambiguous. Most working forensic scientists felt that such methods were best left in the pages of the academic press rather than used in routine case work.

So, after we had determined a bloodstain to be human we attempted to classify it in one of its four main groups A, B, AB, or O. These groups reflect individual characters that are part of the genetic make-up of a human being. They are inherited at conception and they remain fixed throughout life. The ABO factors occur on the surface of the red blood cells. If factor A is present on the surface of the cell the blood group is A. Likewise if factor B is present the blood group is B. If both factors are present the group is AB and if neither is present it is group O.

Determination of the blood group of liquid blood is easy enough. One simply observes how the individual red cells react under the microscope when treated with "antisera". These are liquids which distinguish amongst the four types of red blood cells. Anti-A antiserum causes A cells to aggregate into clumps. Anti-B antiserum clumps B cells. AB cells are clumped by both antisera. Group O cells are clumped by neither. But to do the test this way, one requires intact red blood cells and these are not present in dried blood stains. Certainly the ABO factors are still there, clinging to the microscopic debris of their parent red blood cells, but these cells cannot be reconstituted in the laboratory. How can the forensic scientist detect the blood group factors under such circumstances?

The traditional way in the nineteen fifties was to place the various antisera separately into contact with pieces of the dried bloodstain for a period of time. After this interval of "absorption" the antiserum was removed and examined to see which anti factors had been removed by the bloodstain. This was done by testing the absorbed antisera to see if they had been specifically weakened by contact with the bloodstain. If it was found that the anti-A factor had been removed it was reasoned that this was by its reaction with a group A bloodstain. Similarly if the anti-B factor was removed it was argued that that was because the bloodstain was group B. If both anti factors were removed then the bloodstain was group AB and if neither was removed then it was group O. All this was sound enough in principle but it needed a large amount of bloodstain to work on. Neither was it a very sensitive method. Finally, and worst of all for me, the method represented routine tedium at its most awful. The hallmark of the method was rank upon rank of dozens of small glass tubes. Into each of these tubes had to be pipetted numerous dilutions of the various liquids employed. It was an oppressive affair for anyone so impatient and irritable as I was, but it was a job that had to be done.

So I fell to thinking about finding a simpler and more efficient blood grouping method. In ruminating about this I was aided by the fact that I knew very little about the subject. As one whose training had been largely in the field of the chemistry of plants and micro-organisms I was not steeped in the, largely clinical, published data dealing with blood. Had I been so I might have located a series of articles which, over a period of years, described unsuccessful attempts to do what I proposed to do. At the end of the series of articles the writers concluded that it was not possible. I believe it was the American industrialist Henry Ford who once said that he preferred not to employ experts because they were always giving him reasons why it couldn't be done. Instead he employed enthusiastic amateurs. They didn't know that it couldn't be done, so they went ahead and did it. I think I might have got on quite well with Mr Ford.

So, enveloped in my cloak of ignorance, I thought the problem through and started experimenting. What I was trying to do, remember, was to detect the ABO substances which were left clinging to the microscopic debris of red blood cells. The obvious avenue to explore was to see if I could reconstitute the red cells and change the problem to a simple one in liquid blood grouping. It soon became evident that only an unquenchable optimism and unlimited time could fuel such a line of research. Optimism has never made up a significant part of my character, and I didn't have much time, so I changed my line of attack. I turned to another idea. What if I put the bloodstain and antiserum together and then, instead of the tedious testing to see if the antiserum had been weakened, tested the surface of the bloodstain to see if I could detect any combined antibodies there? Theoretically this was a sound idea but how was I to put it into practice?

The Sceptical Witness

I knew that the antibodies combined slowly but firmly when the temperature was low. I also knew that when the temperature was raised any combined antibodies present tended to be split off from their combined state. So, in outline, all I did was to place the antiserum in contact with the bloodstain for a while and then I washed the treated bloodstain with a cold, dilute, salt solution. Because this liquid was cold it did not split off the antibodies.

After the surplus of antiserum had been removed I then placed a suspension of red blood cells in contact with the treated bloodstain and warmed the mixture up to somewhat above blood heat. Next I allowed it to cool and then I examined the cells for agglutination under the microscope. By ringing the changes on the types of antisera and cells used I was able to demonstrate the presence or absence of particular blood group factors. All this may sound rather complicated but it was much simpler than the old method. The net result was that the amount of effort expended per bloodstain became about a tenth of what it had been before.

I was delighted by the results and, frustrated researcher that I was, I promptly published my findings in the scientific press. Next I decided to subject my new method to a rigorous test by an independent assessor. To do this I asked a friend, a clinical blood researcher with access to a large number of blood samples, to send me bloodstains from one hundred different people. I asked that each should be numbered but otherwise unidentified. Only he would know the blood groups of these test samples.

To group a hundred bloodstains using the old method would have taken me weeks or even months but in the new method I could do bloodstains together in batches. In this way I could subject sets of bloodstains to operations that originally had to be applied to each stain separately. The same manipulations served for the entire batch. An enormous amount of time was saved in this way. I split the hundred bloodstains into six batches of fifteen and one of ten. One batch was examined by me each day for six days. The actual working time required on each batch was no more than two hours but this had to be timed at intervals throughout the day. At other times I was free to do unrelated tasks. Not everything went well. We were an operational laboratory and case work had to come first. Because of this I had to abandon two batches when pressing casework problems intruded. Nevertheless, of the remaining seventy bloodstains on which grouping tests were completed I was able to return results for sixty eight. The other two bloodstains failed to react for technical reasons. All the results proved to be correct and so ABO bloodstain grouping methods moved into a new era. The method was swiftly adopted by the other British forensic science laboratories and then it spread world wide. I called the new method the "Absorption-Elution test".

There were some human aspects of the affair of course. When I published my research results, in the form of two short notes in *Nature*, my chief assistant, a man of a discerning character and highly qualitative expression, articulated his disbelief at the sparse form of my publication. To paraphrase, he told me I was foolish to publish only in the form of a few paragraphs and that I should follow the usual habit of scientists and write a thesis on the subject. I demurred and said my priority would be clearly established by the two notes. He proved right of course and, soon afterwards, the crop of derivative articles published by others obscured the origins of the method. Surprisingly this did not occur outside the United Kingdom. Articles originating from overseas nearly always indicated the true genesis of the method.

A prophet is not without honour, save in his own country and in his own house.

The classical version of scientific research demands that when a new technique is published in the field of applied science then anyone else who wishes to use the method should first perform it strictly as described by the originator. Only after this has been done should any scientist seek to modify the method. In practice I've seldom known this occur. What usually happens is that on reading an article the average applied scientist thinks "Ah, I'm sure that would work better if I changed it in such and such a way". So he goes ahead and changes it. As a consequence he never really gets to know whether the modified technique is better or worse than the original. In addition he has a new technique to publish under his own name. The tendency is to modify then verify instead of verify then modify.

Furthermore if it happens he works in a very distinguished institution then something of the reputation of the institution rubs off on to the derivative article, irrespective of its intrinsic worth. This is a general point that I make and it is not individually addressed. However if the cap fits then you are more than welcome to go ahead and wear it. It is only fair to say that such caps usually fit several heads.

It was only some years later that I realised that the article describing the grouping of the hundred bloodstains was probably the first published example of a "blind" test being applied to a forensic science technique. Note my caution in using the word "probably". It is not possible for anyone to read all the relevant scientific articles ever produced and it is easy to miss something. Nevertheless at the time when the article was published the subject of blind tests was totally unfashionable and it took many years for it to become the integral part of forensic science that it is today. One made a great play on individual "integrity" and it was felt that such a quality needs no test. I am sure that integrity exists, in large measure, in many members of the human race. But it is by no means universal and one should avoid asserting, for whatever reason, that it is.

During the period of attitude change to what became known as "quality assurance" testing, and its introduction into British laboratories, a colleague was transferred to another laboratory where the ethos was a traditional one. The newcomer was one of the younger group of forensic scientists that welcomed the new idea of testing the performance of scientists and techniques. Unhappily his missionary zeal was not shared by all his new colleagues. After a heated discussion on the subject, one, indignant that his integrity should be questioned in such a manner, invited the new arrival outside the laboratory in order to

Chapter Twelve: The Ladder of Expertise

clarify the issue. Hardly a scientific test but then, scientists are human.

Perhaps my least favourite type of case during my years of operational casework in the Harrogate laboratory was the examination of human head hairs. Unfortunately such cases occurred fairly frequently. They generally took the form of a comparison of a hair, or hairs, from a crime scene with a "control" sample of hair taken from the head of a suspect. My job then was to give a considered opinion of the likelihood of the crime scene sample originating from the head of the suspect. To do the job properly required a long time at the microscope and a series of repetitive comparisons within each sample, and between the two samples, of hair. The problem is that to gain a good idea of the microscopic structure of hair requires it to be magnified to an extent that one can see only a small part of the hair shaft. But human head hair varies in its nature along the length of the shaft and so one must spend a great deal of time moving the sample around under the microscope. If one adds to this the fact that even one person's hair may vary widely across his head then the difficulties can be appreciated.

Nowadays in many cases the problem can be approached by DNA analysis. This is done by extracting the small amounts of DNA that occur in hair roots, or the even smaller amounts that occur in the hair shaft, and examining the extracts by the highly discriminating methods of molecular biology. These methods provide evidence of a much higher probative value than we were ever able to produce in those early days using our microscopes. Elderly (I first wrote the word as "old" but my wife changed it) forensic scientists such as I tend to look at these new methods with an envious eye and conclude that we were born too soon. But equally, present day forensic scientists should occasionally pause in their labours and give a thought to their predecessors. It was we who cleared away so much brushwood from the fields of forensic science at the scene and in the laboratory. Only in this way were essential problems highlighted, questions asked, and solutions made possible.

The Sceptical Witness

Not that all the problems with physical evidence were technical ones. One must remember the chain of evidence which stretches all the way from the scene of crime and the suspect(s) all the way through the laboratory to the witness box. Considering the nature of this chain it is not surprising that things occasionally go wrong.

In one case of housebreaking the criminal made his exit at speed through a bedroom window when he was disturbed. In doing so he left his cap behind in the bedroom. The police soon found a suspect for the offence, but he denied that he was involved. The police asked him for a sample of his head hair which he willingly gave and which they then submitted to the laboratory. They also sent the cap which they recovered from the scene. I examined the cap and found some human head hairs inside it. Next I examined the sample of hair from the head of the suspect and found that the hairs came from a dog. This surprised me. For a moment I imagined the advent of high scientific distinction for me as the scientist who first discovered a dog-haired man. After a little thought about the matter however I concluded that this was one of the less likely explanations for my findings.

So I rang the police officer in the case and explained what I had found. I then asked the officer if he had taken the sample of head hair from the suspect himself. He replied that he had not but that he had been present when the suspect pulled it from his own head. So I asked the officer to go back and take another sample. This time he should pull it out for himself and not let the suspect handle it. He agreed to do this and, in due course, the sample of hair arrived at the laboratory. On this occasion the "sample of head hair" proved to be normal human head hair and it was similar to that in the cap.

I was beginning to enjoy all this and it was with relish that I wrote my report for the court. I said in my report that the hair from the cap was normal human head hair. I said that the first "control" sample of head hair was dog hair but that the second "control" sample was normal human head hair and it was similar to that found in the cap. Then I waited my call to court with gleeful anticipation. After a while it came and off I went to a small Yorkshire coastal town to give evidence before the magistrates. Sitting in the witness waiting room I cheerfully wondered what effect my report would have on the court. The case started and then the blow fell. The accused pleaded guilty and I never did get into the witness box.

Chatting about the case later with the officer concerned we pieced together the elements of the mystery. The story unfolded as follows. When the police officer went to the house of the accused to request a sample of hair, the first time, he was courteously received. However the suspect requested a moment before giving the sample of hair because there was something simmering on the hob in the kitchen and he wished to turn the heat down. He returned after a short time and, in the presence of the officer, appeared to pull a tuft of hair from his own head. But what in fact he had done was to pull a handful of hair from his own dog, the poor beast, which was asleep in the kitchen. He then palmed this and led the police officer to believe that it was his own by pretending to pull it from his head. It was with some hilarity that the police officer and I concluded that such acts tended to destroy ones trust in human nature. I didn't stay to find out what the magistrates thought about it all. I had work to do in the laboratory.

The above case description is one example of the many thousands which have been dealt with by forensic scientists which fall under the heading of "transfer traces". But transfer traces need not necessarily be of hair. They can be of blood, semen, clothing fibres, glass particles, paint chips, wood splinters, or of a host of other substances which happen to be around at the moment a crime is committed. One case of assault in which I was a witness will give an illustration of this.

A young woman was alone in her first floor flat. She was in bed and asleep. The time was in the early hours of the morning. An intruder shinned up the fall pipe and gained entrance to the flat though the kitchen window. As he passed through the kitchen he picked up a milk bottle from the table. He then went into the woman's bedroom and struck her sleeping head with the bottle, which broke.

The Sceptical Witness

Thereupon she awoke and, being made of the stuff of which so many Yorkshire women seem to be made, she immediately assessed the situation, took the bedside alarm clock and belaboured her attacker vigorously about the head with it. This she did to very good effect. Indeed the upshot was such that after a while the assailant gave up the struggle and retreated. One presumes that his motive for the attack was sexual and that, not surprisingly, he lost his motivation. The scene was generously sprayed with blood and glass particles before the assailant made good his escape whence he had entered.

The police soon found a suspect with head injuries, arrested him and then sent various samples into the laboratory. These included the man's clothing, the woman's night clothing and bedclothing, and the remnants of the alarm clock and the milk bottle. The blood on the man's clothing fell into two clusters of stains; one around his collar and one around his cuffs. That around his collar was the same blood group as his own and different from the woman's. That around his cuffs was the same blood group as the woman's and different from his own.

On the woman's night clothing the blood around the neck region was the same group as her own blood as was the blood on the pillow. Elsewhere on her clothing, and spread around the bedclothing, there were bloodstains which were of the same group as the man's. From the man's clothing were recovered down feathers similar to those from the eiderdown on the woman's bed. Also recovered from the surface of the man's clothing were two types of glass spicules, one matching the glass from the milk bottle, and one matching the glass from the alarm clock face. Furthermore, on gaining entrance to and leaving the flat, the intruder left his footprints in the kitchen sink. These matched the shoes of the suspect.

But this was not all. This plethora of transfer trace evidence was supplemented by an intriguing discovery. I noticed a nondescript stain on the right forearm of the jacket of the suspect. Making an inspired guess I analysed an extract using the agar plug method mentioned earlier and I proved the present of cow protein. I also established the

Chapter Twelve: The Ladder of Expertise

presence of lactose, otherwise milk sugar. Evidently what had happened was that, when the assailant had picked up the milk bottle, it wasn't empty. So, on lifting it to strike the woman, the milk ran out and down his arm. Every single case of transfer evidence is, at least in detail, unique but this was the only case I ever examined where the transfer of cow's milk traces proved of value as evidence. I attended court for a pre-trial conference with the lawyer who expressed his misgivings to me in the following words: "I'm worried about this case Mr Kind, there's precious little evidence". The court did not share his misgivings and the accused was convicted.

The tendency for messages to become distorted when transmitted through several stages is legendary. At school I remember being taught the dangers of verbal distortion and the example used was the old story, doubtless apocryphal, of a despatch sent in the First World War. This was sent verbally and sequentially along a line of troops, from one to the next to its destination. What started as:

"going to advance, send reinforcements"

ended up as:

"going to a dance, send three and fourpence"

This ancient and unpretentious example is as good as any I've heard although, in these decimalised days, its impact would doubtless be less than it was in my childhood. But other forms of distortion are common in all aspects of life. Some are deliberate and some are fortuitous. One of the latter occurs when specialists view real everyday problems through the distorting mirror provided by their own training and professional affiliations.

In the early days of forensic science such professional distortion was probably much more current than nowadays. We were still at the time when the influence of the old directors, the ex academics, was still dominant. Thus we were all either biologists or chemists with an occasional genuflection made in the direction of the physicists. "Chemists" usually took on the task of dealing with cases involving motor vehicle accidents. This was reasonable considering the amount of evidence that could be extracted by an experienced forensic chemist from transfer traces, which usually consisted of paint and glass fragments and oil stains. Should a question of transferred blood be also involved there was no difficulty in recognising it as such and passing it over to a biological colleague. But, if the transfer trace were less common (*vide supra*, cow's milk transfer) then the best method to use could be obscured by a professional barrier.

In one case of what was known in those days as "motor manslaughter", the deceased, an old lady, was carrying her shopping bag which contained eggs. A dried substance on the suspect car's radiator grill looked as though it might be egg yoke and white. The chemist involved attempted to analyse the residue by the traditional methods of analytical chemistry. They were not up to the task and it was only when the traces were subjected to "biological" methods that the problem was solved. And the methods? Simply the application of the agar jelly plug method, described earlier, to prove bird protein. Next a test to show that blood of any sort was absent and we have a highly probative result for evidence in court. This was not a demarcation dispute. When people are fully busy there is little cause for such disputes to arise. It is simply a small example of how a specialist training can distort the point of view of the observer.

But I do remember one demarcation dispute about this time. This arose when an outside government agency asked me to identify some fibres adhering to a metal fragment and to see if they matched fibres from an upholstered seat. The problem had arisen during the investigation of an aircraft crash in which there was suspicion that a terrorist bomb had been responsible. I identified the fibres from the metal fragment under the microscope and noted that they were the same type as those in the upholstered seat. At the same time I observed that the fibres on the fragment were distributed in a peculiar fashion. Closely impacted on one side of the particle they were comparatively loose, in the manner of an artist's brush, on the other. From this I opined that the particle had struck the fabric at high velocity in the manner one would expect should the particle be shrapnel from a bomb.

The reaction from the recipient of my report was swift and condescending. Would I kindly stick to my field of expertise and leave him to his? My own response was equally nimble and, as I remember it, outstandingly evocative. I subsequently learned that my message had been sanitised before despatch by the laboratory police liaison officer. He was a man of infinite courtesy who had a practised eye for anything which might cause problems in the future.

The man from the other ministry was typical of the one-case forensic scientist. His life of routine engineering problems was about to be lightened by his day in court as an expert witness and he was not going to have any outsider muscling in on the act. Unsurprisingly I was not called to give evidence on the identity of the fibres. Presumably someone did. Presumably that someone was an "expert". The problems that arise when amateurs deal with expert problems are legion. The problems that arise when specialists deal with specialist problems can be equally misleading. There is an infinity of standpoints from which any practical problem can be viewed and only experience and goodwill can provide the solutions. Choosing an expert sometimes begs the question.

Interfaces alter cases (Kind)

Then there is the connected problem of the use of scientific expertise in management. I am probably in a minority in my profession when I say that I do not believe that a "scientific" training is necessarily a suitable basis for management duties. As time passes and more people become "qualified" in "science" this becomes even more evident. Make of the quotes what you will.

During my career I have seen some scientists make an excellent job of management. I have seen others make a total hash of it. My attempts to correlate scientific aptitude with management ability have led to no results worth publicising. For what it's worth, and with no research results to bolster my subjective view, I would say if you want to get a good grounding for management then study the classics. Come to think of it, most of my administrative superiors in the large government department for which I worked, were classics men. Perhaps they got to me more skilfully than I realised. But I must retreat to safer ground.

Chapter Thirteen: Coincidence and Paradigm

It is a fallacy to believe that the criminal trial is a replay of the investigation. This misconception is not restricted to the general public but is common also amongst scientists. I suspect that the delusion is even entertained by some lawyers, but here one must be careful. With lawyers one never knows. It is usually conceded that such replays are to some extent formalised to ensure that evidence given to the court is factual and relevant. But "factual " and "relevant" can be question begging words

How different the investigation is from the trial can be best demonstrated by a thought experiment. Imagine yourself to be a senior police investigator and that you have just received a telephone call about a body that has been found in suspicious circumstances. Now imagine yourself being driven to the scene (a senior police investigator would probably not drive himself) and on the way you are ruminating upon what you might find when you arrive. Think up your own circumstances be they day/night, wet/dry, summer/winter, light/dark, city/country and the many others circumstances from which you may choose. Take all this against a background known to the investigator including a possible developing series of murders.

Imagine where the investigator finds the body be it in a ditch, at the side of a road, stuffed down a manhole, in bed, in a carboot or in a host of other circumstances and against a myriad of backgrounds. The scene of crime officer is in bed with flu and the forensic pathologist is in Tenerife, resulting in the necessity to find substitutes. Is the body that of a male or female (not universally and immediately evident under such circumstances), is the death natural, accident, homicide or suicide? What is the identity of the body and can it be connected with a recent missing persons report? Imagine all the above circumstances and a horde of others and, assuming the chain leads to a conclusion that the deceased is a murder victim, then what mental steps must the investigator consider in his consideration of the central question of whodunit? After calling in Kipling's Six Honest Serving Men (Chapter Ten, Red Herrings and Jigsaws) let us assume that the investigator has successfully placed the killer in the dock on a charge of murder.

The Sceptical Witness

But how does the investigator know the man in the dock is the murderer? His knowledge and confidence in the matter stem from his experience, the manpower and support systems he can draw upon and the wealth of information which has flooded in, which he has distilled into evidence. The question is no longer one of an inductive answer to a whodunit? question, but of a deductive test of a did-he-do-it? question. It is only by this refining process that the court can receive a problem of manageable proportions. The court is not there to determine, except on a very limited basis, the "truth" of any matter, whatever "truth" may be. The court is simply there to determine if a defined criminal charge, made against a named individual, has been established beyond reasonable doubt. The trial is a test of the belief of the investigator that he has got the right man.

And herein lies one source of misconceived reformist proposals to improve, and render more precise, the criminal trial process. The reformers tend to equate the discovery process in science with the trial process in the criminal court. Unhappily they seek to do this by removing the court proceedings from the comprehension of the community at large. This they do not only by advocating more specialist input to the criminal trial (which can be a very good thing) but also by arguing for more specialist intrusion into the decision making process itself. This is a consequence of the fact that the specialist techniques they advocate are beyond the comprehension of the average lawyer, magistrate or jury member. A necessary qualification for criminal trial reformers, particularly those with a "scientific" bent, would be to require them to sit through, but not participate in, twenty hotly contested criminal cases. In this way not only would they better grasp the real nature of the problem the court has to grapple with but they might show less tendency to propose that the problems of decision making in court are best left to the great, the good and the expert. The unrealism of some would-be reformers is beyond belief, at least beyond mine. But for the moment let us return to sanity and the realities of the court room.

Chapter Thirteen: Coincidence and Paradigm

A well presented prosecution case can leave listeners, and that includes the bench and jury, all but convinced that there can be little defence against such a charge and such evidence. Happily a well prepared and presented defence case can also leave them amazed that they had failed to appreciate the fallacies in the arguments of the prosecution. The fact that these experiences are sometimes highly amusing should not blind one to the lessons which may be learned from such case histories. Consider the following two examples. Although both cases might be taken as minor items in the criminal calendar this should not obscure the fact that the principles they illustrate are common to all criminal trials. Both accounts are factual.

Case No 1. Circumstances. A police officer was on duty in the early hours of the morning when he heard the sound of breaking glass. He traced this to the rear of a clothing warehouse where he found a broken window. Hard against this was a large wooden box which had obviously been used as an aid to gain entrance through the window. The officer climbed through the window into the warehouse and spent some time searching the premises but found nothing. He was on the point of leaving when he heard a noise from above and noticed a trapdoor in the ceiling and a ladder leading to it. He climbed the ladder and gained access to a loft where he found the defendant and arrested him. The defendant was wearing an expensive overcoat which was subsequently proved to originate from the warehouse stock. He was charged with burglary. At the trial he pleaded Not Guilty.

It would be instructive for the reader to pause here and consider what possible innocent explanations the defendant might produce to explain the circumstances in which the police officer found him. This should then be compared with the defendant's own story, which is outlined as follows in the form of a paraphrase of his own words.

The Defendant's Story: *"I had been out at the pub with some friends and, after closing time, went home with one of them for another drink and a chat. I left my friend's house in the early hours of the morning and walked home through the back streets. During my journey I heard the sound of breaking glass and went to investigate. I found a large box against the broken window of a clothing warehouse and felt it my duty, in the absence of a police officer, to investigate and, if possible, to effect a citizen's arrest.*

"I entered the warehouse and searched it but could find nothing. On the point of leaving I heard a noise from above and formed the view that someone was hiding in the loft. I began to climb the ladder into the loft when the thought struck me that I would most likely get my best suit dirty whilst searching the loft.

"Because of this, and because I was acting on behalf of the community and not of myself, I took an overcoat from a nearby rack and put it on. I then climbed up and entered the loft. I made a thorough search but could find nothing unusual and I concluded that the intruder, if there had been one, had made good his escape before my arrival. As I made to leave the loft the police officer stuck his head through the trapdoor."

Case No 2. Circumstances. At 2pm on a bright sunny day a police car was cruising slowly down a gently sloping road when the two officers aboard noticed a car being driven erratically towards them. As the car approached it suddenly swerved over to the wrong side of the road and struck the police car a violent, glancing blow. The officers turned to pursue the offending car only to find that it was now stationary in the middle of the road. They got out and, as they approached the car on foot, it began to roll backwards. Pulling open the driver's door the officers found the driver slumped over the steering wheel. They applied the handbrake and then took the driver into custody where he was charged with a variety of motoring offences. These included driving under the influence of alcohol whilst unlicensed and uninsured to drive. The defendant made no statement. In court he pleaded Not Guilty to all charges and he produced no witnesses. Once again the reader might wish to stop here and speculate what possible defence could be produced against the charges. Then he should read on and compare his own notions with the defendant's story which, once more, is given in a paraphrase of the defendant's own words.

Chapter Thirteen: Coincidence and Paradigm

The Defendant's Story: *"On the day in question I went to market as a passenger in the car which was driven by a friend who is a qualified driver. Because it was market day the pubs were open all day and I had a lot to drink. On the way back home my friend stopped the car at the top of a hill and got out to go to a nearby public lavatory. Unfortunately he did not apply the handbrake properly and, after his departure, the car began to move off downhill.*

"As the car gathered speed I reached over from the passenger seat, took the steering wheel, and struggled to gain control. The car reached the bottom of the hill and its impetus carried it up the hill on the other side. It was then I noticed the police car coming towards me. I did my best to avoid it but it was very difficult to steer from the passenger seat and I hit the police car a glancing blow. My own vehicle gradually lost momentum and slowed to a halt. It was at this point that I managed to struggle into the driving seat. Exhausted by my efforts, I slumped forward over the driving wheel. Then the police officer opened the car door."

When the defendant had finished his story the Bench posed the obvious question to him. Why had he not produced his friend as a witness? The reason, replied the defendant with disarming frankness, was that he thought the magistrates would believe his story.

But humour and ingenuity should not be allowed to obscure the overriding lesson that no case is indefensible. Neither should it be. The defendant must be allowed every opportunity to demolish the prosecution case (note that I do not say "to establish his innocence" because that is not the essence of a criminal defence).

Society has to make decisions through its criminal courts and society is imperfect. There will always be faulty convictions and faulty acquittals. Decisions based upon testimonial evidence in court always carry the potential for error and it is difficult to see how it can ever be otherwise. Erroneous verdicts might be reduced in number in some gross Orwellian world which employs a 24 hour surveillance of the citizen. But even here errors will never be eliminated. Intent is invisible to video cameras. Keeping in mind the fact that an accused person is not compelled to explain his actions in a criminal court it is often to his advantage to do so. This is what the accused were trying to do. Such explanations might be successful or not (both the accused were convicted) but the essence of the attempt is to establish that the allegedly criminal act was an innocent one. It was, each said, an act which was, coincidentally, observed under conditions which suggested that it was criminal.

Such attempts, as in these two examples, sometimes necessitate a degree of optimism and ingenuity possessed by few of us. But this should not be allowed to obscure the fact that in the criminal trial the prosecution treats the events outlined in evidence as causal, whereas the defence may seek to demonstrate that they were coincidental.

Words, words, words. When any author is writing for instruction he is in danger of losing his audience if he introduces concepts and words unfamiliar to his audience. "Cause" and "coincidence" are hardly unfamiliar words but in seeking to use them in a conceptually novel situation he may render them so. In an attempt to keep the subject on more recognisable terrain I propose to give some examples additional to the two case histories already given.

A little while ago I was reading an interesting account of an event in the sixteenth century. The precise details escape me because, like so many other scientists, I have never learned invariably to employ the habit of making a note at the time. Life would have been rendered tedious had I done so. Nevertheless I can remember the essence of the story clearly.

It appears that Henry the Eighth, an English monarch famed for frequent marriage and the subsequent elimination of spouses, like all managers was faced with many daily problems of enquiry and decision. One of these was to establish the reason for the silting up of a particular English south coast port. So he sent a commissioner down to investigate the matter.

Chapter Thirteen: Coincidence and Paradigm

In his notes of evidence the commissioner recorded the various views of local citizens on the cause of the silting up of the harbour. One old man was quite clear on the cause. It was because a certain church steeple had been built at the time. Prior to the appearance of the steeple the harbour had been clear. After the steeple had been built the harbour progressively silted up. *Post hoc ergo propter hoc* as the philosophers say, "after this therefore because of this". The building of the church steeple caused the silting up of the harbour. Few would believe that there could possibly be any connection between the two events but it is not difficult to think up a sequence of events where there might have been, unlikely though such episodes may be. Remember the case of the radio waves that passed through the ether, described in Chapter 10? The purpose of scientific thinking is to distinguish consequence from subsequence.

Forty years ago I was sitting in an English magistrates court listening to the clerk as he read out the deposition of the complainant. The charge was one of assault occasioning grievous bodily harm. The complainant had been subjected to an attack during which he had been struck on the head with a bottle, which broke on impact. As the clerk intoned the words "... the bottle broke and the glass showered around my shoulders..." the light bulb above the clerk's head dropped out of its socket and smashed on the deposition lying on the desk before him. Visibly shaken, it was some time before the clerk was able to regain his composure and resume reading.

Consider now the following further experience. Some time ago I drove to my son's house via the A1 trunk road in north east England. This is a route with which I am very familiar and, after a period of driving, I fell into a reverie. Those travelling familiar routes will recognise the phenomenon which is often referred to as "going into auto-pilot".

I began to think about the remarkable wartime experience of a Royal Air Force bomber crew member who, faced with the choice of burning to death or bailing out without a parachute, chose the latter course. A remarkable series of events saved his life. I had not thought about the event for many years and I've no idea why I began to think about it on that occasion.

On arriving at my son's house he gave me a birthday present. This was a newly published book which I opened at random, that is to say that I believed that my action was unguided. It fell open at a page where the event I have just mentioned was described. The title of the book was "Coincidence". To the best of my knowledge I had not heard of the book before. Neither had I any idea I was to receive it, or any other book for that matter, as a birthday present. What is remarkable about this group of occurrences is that it was a double coincidence. Not only did the book fall open at the description of the event in my reverie but, almost as if to emphasise the incident, the book was entitled "Coincidence".

Can one predict the probability of such very complex events with any accuracy? It seems most unlikely that this is possible. The problem is that such events must be classified in a framework of other occurrences of the "same" incident. But one-off incidents such as these do not lend themselves to such grouping. If the incident can be established to be a combination of more elementary incidents of a higher frequency of occurrence then something may be done. But such analysis doesn't seem to be possible in many real life events of the complexity either of the one just described or of the "court clerk and light bulb" example.

Nevertheless "simple" events can often be extracted from complex real life circumstances and then treated statistically. The existence of the insurance and betting industries depends upon this fact. There are few things as unequivocal as death and the winner of the 3-45 race at Sandown Park. One might even seek, statistically, to prove a causal connection, or correlation, between the two. But caution is necessary. If we search for a connection between deaths and the winner of the 3-45 at Sandown, the fact that *Nobbut Just* came first may not be so relevant as the fact that *Joy for Ever* came last. But most states and events in the natural world are "clustered" in the macroscopic sense. Everyday experience leads us to

Chapter Thirteen: Coincidence and Paradigm

accept and expect that certain patterns re-occur time and time again. These commonly recurring patterns allow us to abstract our own particular mental models of real processes.

Abstracting my own mental model I believe that the investigation of a crime and the consequent criminal trial are best considered, conceptually, as a book of three chapters: *The Problem to Find, The Decision to Charge* and *The Problem to Prove*. All three chapters contain elements of induction and deduction. Induction consists of reasoning from the particular to the general. Deduction consists of reasoning from the general to the particular. However the first chapter, the investigation, requires predominantly inductive reasoning in that it considers how various pieces of evidence combine to point to a particular culprit. The second chapter is something of a hybrid and it represents the fundamental change in mental attitude which is required in the change from a mainly inductive, to a mainly deductive, reasoning approach to evidence. The third chapter, the criminal trial, is mainly deductive in character in that it considers each piece of evidence in the light of the hypothesis (i.e. the criminal charge) that a named accused person is guilty of the offence. Individuals who are actively concerned with crime investigation and the criminal trial, a group which includes trial lawyers, police officers and forensic scientists, tend to develop a mental model, or paradigm, of the process in which they are so deeply involved. This paradigm is the product of the personal character of the individual professional, together with his background, education, training and experience and it provides a norm against which he can judge new cases. It is not possible to act in a state of mental isolation when thinking out new experiences, we must check the new facts against what we know already.

As ones professional experience grows it becomes refined to give a general mental model in which the non-essentials are removed and the general features thrown into greater relief because of the absence of contingent detail. This is the paradigm I speak of and it represents the distillation, from a large number of sense impressions, of an integrated mental picture free of chance particularities. A paradigm is something which has survived a repeated checking against individual experience and which has grown and consolidated thereby. A well-established paradigm, which is self consistent and provides a rational reflection of the outside world, may even spread and be adopted by others to become part of standard teaching and textbook material. However it must be admitted that even greatly experienced crime investigators, a term which I take to include forensic scientists, can be hard put to describe their own paradigms of crime investigation and the criminal trial. Very often they are content to work on an instinctive and intuitive basis rather than to agonise about conceptual structure. Involvement in the demanding world of crime investigation and the criminal trial leaves little time for theorising. An unfortunate consequence of this lack of interest in concept is that it leaves a clear field for those with only academic or administrative experience of the subject to exercise a disproportionate influence in print. Such a lack of hands-on practical experience allows the theoretician to produce neat and attractive conceptual models which result in conclusions which are quite inconsistent with practical observations.

To help rectify the balance I propose to outline my own paradigm of crime investigation and the criminal trial (already touched upon in Chapter Ten: Red Herrings and Jigsaws). I developed this during a long career in forensic science, and so it may be devoid of some of the theoretical (occasionally almost metaphysical) niceties employed by those whose thinking is not practically constrained by the real world of events. The account represents the crystallization and refinement consequent upon much experience and thinking. It does not seek to provide a definitive description of the situation but it provides, I believe, a much more realistic and useful framework than some other common views. The treatment I adopt considers investigation and trial as two separate features of the same process. They are respectively the "problem to find" and the "problem to prove" aspects. The idea that the problem is conceptually best handled as two aspects of a single operation can be obscured, in practical affairs, by the fact that the two parts, investigation and trial, are largely serviced by two different groups of professionals, respectively police and lawyers. My approach

Chapter Thirteen: Coincidence and Paradigm

to the problem makes no pretence to completeness in detail, neither does it deny that other paradigms may be better models for the mental backdrop which we all must use when considering observations. It is for the individual reader to decide which paradigm suits him best.

A note of warning is appropriate here. It is a human trait to favour ones own paradigm at the expense of others which compete with it. Occasionally this trait can result in an individual's refusal to consider, or perhaps even to notice, evidence or argument which conflict with his own views. This is a pity. The repeated checking against other paradigms is a fascinating and revealing process. No intellectual model has general value if it is not the product of a thought process which is tempered by observation, deduction and by comparison with competing points of view. I consider the investigation of a crime, and its consequential trial, as consisting of a sequence of three main chapters. I use the word "chapter" in preference to "stage", "phase", "aspect" or "step" because it seems to me that the ideas of words, pages, and sequence, together with the capacity to turn back the pages to check facts, seems particularly apposite here. Even the idea of turning the pages forward has some application when one considers the process of reasoning from the known facts; of deducing consequences.

The mental processing of evidence in both crime investigation and the criminal trial are repetitive processes, not simple ones. The moment a piece of information is received by a human mind it becomes available for cross checking against what is already known. Obviously an investigator, or advocate, must perform certain operations in sequence. These operations are those which experience, or rules of evidence, or logical necessity, dictate must be done in such and such a way. Nevertheless the mind of the investigator, advocate, judge or juryman does not proceed in a columnar fashion. It roves in a very large number of dimensions, including time, and it checks and cross-checks facts against allegations in countless ways. One of the best descriptions of this process comes from the pen of the nineteenth century thinker and writer J.H. Newman:

The mind ranges to and fro, and spreads out, and advances forward with a quickness which has become a proverb, and a subtlety and versatility which baffle investigation. It passes on from point to point, gaining one by some indication; another on a probability; then availing itself of an association; then falling back on some received law; next seizing on testimony, then committing itself to some popular impression, or some inward instinct, or some obscure memory; and thus it makes progress not unlike a clamberer on a steep cliff, who, by quick eye, prompt hand, and firm foot, ascends how he knows not himself, by personal endowments and by practice, rather than by rule...

There is a danger, in quoting writings like this, that some of my scientific colleagues may accuse me of being "unscientific" but I can only answer that, of all types of scientist, the forensic scientist must know that the output of his deliberations is destined to become the input of forums which are compelled to think and act in terms of daily experience, not in terms of laboratory science and mathematics. I omit in this treatment any consideration of what might be called the "preface" to the three chapters. This is the problem of deciding if a crime has been committed which is a more difficult problem than imagined by those professionally unconnected with crime investigation. So, to reiterate, the chapters are: (1) the problem to find, (2) the decision to charge, (3) the problem to prove.

The first chapter in the sequence of the criminal investigation and trial starts when the investigator begins his search for the criminal, and it ceases when the investigator becomes confident that he has found him. This moment, when the investigator becomes sure that he has the right culprit, is a very important one in the crime investigation sequence. Ideally, of course, this ending of the first chapter, this moment of crystallization of the investigator's views, should immediately be followed by the preferral of the charge. In practice there seems little doubt that the two events are usually separated by a period of time during which the investigator elaborates his case against the suspect further. This is often because the rules of evidence preclude the investigator from introducing in evidence all the information which was available to him when he decided he had found the right culprit.

Chapter Thirteen: Coincidence and Paradigm

During this first chapter of crime investigation the thinking of the investigator largely follows the patterns of inductive inference in which he reasons from the particular to the general. He reasons largely by analogy based upon his experience and his mind checks the details of evidence and tries to fit them into an overall pattern. At this stage his thoughts tend to be of the type "this looks as though it might be a job done by X" or "perhaps group Y is involved" or "I wonder if Z is out of prison yet?". These ideas flood his thoughts in the form of a series of, not necessarily mutually exclusive, alternative hypotheses which becomes his universe of mental discourse. The richness of this universe is dependent upon the quality and amount of information which reaches him, together with his own perception of the information and his capacity to process it effectively. High grade intellect, together with a good education, followed by substantial training and experience are the requisites here. In addition, the investigator must have an intelligent and well-trained support staff so that the information which is supplied to him is as little flawed as possible.

The second chapter in the crime investigation and criminal trial process begins from the moment when the investigator becomes sure he has the right culprit, and it lasts until the moment when the trial begins. It is during this period that the investigator acts to refine and perfect the case he has elaborated against the accused. During either of these first two chapters the investigator may pose questions to the forensic scientist which deal with "who is guilty of the crime?", although in the second chapter such questions tend more to deal with "what further evidence can I adduce to support my view that X is guilty of the crime?", rather than with "have I got the right man?" In other words, during the second chapter of investigation the investigator tends to search for evidence corroborating a decision he has already made. This is a potentially dangerous time both for the investigator and for the forensic scientist in that positive feedback may compound a cyclic thought process. If one is already convinced that an individual is guilty then interpretation of evidence may be carried out within too restricted a mental framework.

So, at the margin between the first and second chapters of the investigation the investigator's attitude changes from a largely inductive one, reasoning from the particular to the general ("based upon the evidence which I am uncovering, who is responsible for this crime?") to a largely deductive one which reasons from the general to the particular ("what are the individual strengths and weaknesses of my case against this particular man?"). It must be admitted that induction and deduction can seldom, if ever, be practised entirely separately. Furthermore it is common, in retrospect, for human beings to put a precise deductive gloss on a procedure (the derivation of a mathematical equation is another good example) after a rather untidy process of discovery. Nevertheless the distinction between the first two chapters is, I believe, a real and valuable one.

The third and last chapter of the investigation is the trial itself and it is here that the prosecution puts its case that the accused is guilty as charged. It is at the beginning of this stage that the prosecution, so to speak, irrevocably puts all its money on one horse, the case against the accused. The charge is simply a hypothesis that the accused is guilty of the offence and the court, sitting as a tribunal of fact, is there to decide if this hypothesis of guilt will stand up to open debate in court. In the criminal trial the prosecution proposes and the court disposes. The magistrates or jury are enjoined to consider the accused to be innocent until proved guilty, whereas the prosecution is under no such restriction. The essence of the prosecution case is that the accused is certainly guilty, the allegation is absolute, there is no vacillation in the matter.

Thereafter, contrary to popular belief, the trial is not so much a sequential building up of evidence, because all the prosecution evidence is already implicit in the charge. The charge would not have been made had the evidence not been available to base it upon. Rather the trial is a series of tests of the prosecution's hypothesis that the accused is guilty of the criminal offence under consideration. With each new piece of prosecution evidence, there occurs a consideration of its relevance in relation to the hypothesis of guilt and, if the evidence sur-

Chapter Thirteen: Coincidence and Paradigm

vives the test in the minds of the jury, then it becomes *part* of the hypothesis of guilt in that it adds flesh to the bare bones of the criminal charge. In other words, each prosecution witness's evidence is considered as a statement that is potentially falsifiable. Remember the prosecution evidence is the evidence upon which the charge itself has already been based, and it is of value in court only inasmuch as it is shown to be a sound element of the charge. If the prosecution case receives a battering in court then what is left, and that upon which the court makes up its mind, is the remnant of the hypothesis of guilt which has survived the attack. Once again, I find it useful to visualise the situation as a skeletal charge wearing evidential flesh. If the flesh is hanging off the skeleton in tatters then that is the mental image which remains to the jury.

In the first chapter we deal with the problem to find, a largely inductive process, a reasoning from the particular to the general, a real-time search for a criminal, a piecing together of points and details of evidence on an advancing front, a period of interrogations within a much looser framework of rules than that governing cross-examination in court. The first chapter ends when the investigator personally concludes that he has found the criminal.

The second chapter is something of a hybrid and it represents the period of tidying up of loose ends of evidence and the making of formal decisions, including the formulation of the charge, and preparations for the court trial.

The third chapter is the trial itself which is the problem to prove. The criminal trial is, in my view, simply a public test of the charge, an assessment of the soundness of the hypothesis of guilt. The formal structure of a criminal trial is a deductive one, it reasons from the general to the particular, from the idea that the accused is the crux of the issue to the particular details of the evidence. Although it is doubtless good practice for the prosecution to tell a chronological story, the court does not have to take the evidence in the same order as events occurred in the committal of the crime; most expert witnesses have experienced giving their evidence "out of turn". In listening to witnesses' evidence, and counsels' speeches, the court mentally roves freely amongst the pages of the three chapters, aided by the faculty of hindsight and checking detail after detail for its consistency with the charge. The function of the court is analogous to doing a jigsaw puzzle with the aid of a picture on the puzzle box lid. The investigator had to do the puzzle without the aid of the picture. The first chapter is concerned with the whodunit? part of the three-chapter sequence. The third chapter is concerned with the did-the-accused-do-it? part.

In what terms should the forensic scientist express his findings? One view which currently seems to be gaining powerful support, is that it is the job of the forensic scientist, in his function as a court witness, to consider the value of his evidence in terms of responsibility for the crime; to measure ".........the probability of the evidence given guilt and the probability of the evidence given innocence....". The ratio of the former to the latter is often called the likelihood ratio.

I believe this view to be fundamentally flawed and that the forensic scientist, in his court duty as an expert witness (as distinct from his job as adviser to the investigator), has no function in assessing questions of "guilt". Even the word "guilt" itself is a model of ambiguity in that it can represent both a state and an operational decision. The assessment of guilt is the business of the court. The job of the forensic scientist is to deal with the problem of whether or not the physical evidence from two evidential sources (e.g. crime scene/accused) arises from the same event; that is to say whether it is of cognate origin or not. As far as the matter of "responsibility" is concerned it is difficult, if not impossible, to imagine any circumstantial evidence which cannot have an interpretation placed upon it which is distinct from that interpretation chosen by the prosecution (Thoreau's famous example of finding a trout in the milk notwithstanding). It is the job of the court, not the scientist, to decide upon the merit of such evidence and upon their relationship to the criminal charge. This does not mean that the scientific witness cannot comment upon such alternative explanations provided he is invited to do so and he frames his replies in terms of

Chapter Thirteen: Coincidence and Paradigm

cognation rather than responsibility.

One might, for example, find a fingerprint from the accused person on a glass found at the scene of a murder. The cognate origin of this scene mark, and a fingerprint taken from the accused, can hardly be disputed in the present state of fingerprint knowledge, but how and when it got on to a glass at the scene can be open to much debate. Possible alternative explanations are always the backdrop of the contested criminal trial and it is within this mental milieu that all decisions of the "what happened?" variety must be made. Both the investigation and trial are carried out by human beings with all their prejudices and other shortcomings. Uncritical belief is prejudice. Uninformed scepticism is prejudice. The major qualification for a juryman or a magistrate or trial lawyer or professional witness is an open, informed and critical mind. And remember that all expert evidence is modulated by the personality of the giver. Personally I believe that the great majority of court experts nowadays are honest people. I believe this for two main reasons. First it is easier to be honest in such a job when one is under close and public gaze. Secondly the existence of such professional bodies as the Forensic Science Society is a powerful influence in weeding out the charlatan.

All proceedings in crime investigation and the criminal trial should, wherever possible, be modulated by the maximum courtesy. Crime and its associated events are often unpleasant, why make it worse? This is a message which would profit many suspects and defendants too, although it is doubtful if many such will read this book.

Many years ago, before the existence of statutory alcohol levels, the opinion of the police surgeon on the state of sobriety or otherwise of the defendant was a powerful influence on the verdict of the court in "driving under the influence" cases. In one such case the police surgeon was called to the police station in the early hours of the morning to examine a tourist who had imbibed all too well. With his pyjamas underneath his suit the police surgeon wearily approached the defendant.

"I'm a doctor" he said.
"You're a bum" was the reply.

The remainder of the examination was carried out in silence and finally the police surgeon left the room to be accosted by the officer in the case.

"Is he drunk, doctor" he said.
"Well, if he isn't now, he will be in court tomorrow morning" was the grim response.

If the reader gains no advantage from this book other than a clear idea of the difference between the "discovery" and the "review" processes in the investigation of crime, I will feel I have succeeded. Public enquiries can expose enormous shortcomings in any field of human endeavour. This is particularly so in the field of crime investigation, even to the extent that the principals themselves may admit they made errors. Yet it seemed like a good idea at the time. Seeking for solutions in a developing situation, with its contemporary pressures, is quite different from the comparatively leisurely pursuit of "fact" by the tribunal or other *post facto* inquiry. Most improvements in human affairs and institutions result from errors which are identified with the benefit of hindsight.

Footnote:

Part of the above chapter is an extract from an article published in the *Journal of the Forensic Science Society* (now *Science and Justice*). For those who wish to read further on the matter the reference is:

Kind S. S.
Journal of the Forensic Science Society, 1994; 34(3): 155-164

Chapter Fourteen: Time to Think

Part of my very active life at Harrogate, in the fifties and sixties, was spent trying to find a charitable foundation willing to set up a research centre for forensic science. Sometimes I appeared to be close to success, but my efforts always ultimately foundered because of the incapacity of the grant giving bodies to consider forensic science as a "real" science rather than as a ragbag of assorted technical methods which just happened to be of value in crime investigation. My argument (perhaps unwisely chosen) that medicine, and indeed any applied field that used scientific methods, could be subject to the same strictures failed to impress the custodians of the charitable coffers.

I was on the verge of giving up when my employers resolved to take a hand in the matter themselves. They decided to set up a forensic science laboratory which was to be free of case work and dedicated entirely to research and development in forensic science. This was exactly what I wanted. I had absolutely no hand in this decision and it was a total surprise to me that such plans were afoot. Indeed it was most unlikely that the Home Office was aware that amongst its staff was one who had been quietly promoting such an idea for years. I certainly hadn't publicised it amongst my colleagues being convinced that the management was far too reactionary to see the virtues of such a scheme. Once again I was quite wrong.

Plans for the new laboratory advanced swiftly, largely under the guidance of its new director designate. He proved to be a colleague of mine who worked in the field of drugs and poisons. He was a most able scientist and I thought the appointment an inspired one. This was especially so because he was a comparatively young man and the usual methods of selection for promotion in those days contained a large element of Buggins' turn. With confidence I awaited the invitation to be deputy director and chief biologist of the new institution. After all, at that time I was the only biologist in the service who had any substantial record of published research. Who else would be qualified to do the work? The weeks passed and no invitation arrived and I was beginning to despair when, finally, the new director arrived at my laboratory and asked me to take on the job. I promptly accepted and began to look forward with enthusiasm to a return to research work after a very long break. Shortly thereafter my ego was bruised when my new boss told me how glad he was that I had accepted. "You see" he said "no-one else wanted it and I was becoming quite desperate". One must forgive him his ineptitude. His mind was quite full of science and it left no room for social niceties.

I remember being puzzled at the time by the lack of information about the discussions which must have taken place leading up to the establishment of the new laboratory. It was almost like a rabbit being produced from a hat. Hey Presto! a new laboratory. Doubtless the mandarins had taken advice from the laboratory directors on the matter but I have no doubt that the major deliberations about, and the final decision on, the desirability of the new unit was taken at a high level in the control rooms of our ministry. Throughout my service I never got the impression that we scientists impressed our administrative masters overmuch although they were well enough schooled not to dream of saying so.

Nevertheless the mandarins, whether they were scientists or not, had a well developed sense of occasion. They were fully aware that the time had come to set up the new unit to provide the missing link in the structure of forensic science. Looking back on these incidents, with the wisdom conferred upon me by hindsight, it becomes evident that, globally speaking (as one does nowadays) in the history of forensic science development the single most influential body has been the Home Office of the United Kingdom. The decisions to set up forensic science laboratories on a national scale, and subsequently to set up the research unit, gave the role model in forensic science to the rest of the world. I sometimes wonder if there was at some time, a forward looking civil service mandarin who, single handed, convinced his more reactionary and classically educated colleagues to take this revolutionary step. Imaginative ideas are seldom seeded, or fostered, by the committee process.

Chapter Fourteen: Time to Think

Perhaps it was the large and varied experience in administrative problems, already dealt with by the Home Office, which provided the fertile ground for the new ideas to grow in. This is because the Home Office, which is the British civil service equivalent of the "interior" departments of other countries, deals with such a huge range of domestic matters that its staff tends to accumulate a wider outlook than most civil servants. During the early years of my service the extent of its responsibilities was even more kaleidoscopic than nowadays and it stretched from the police forces at the one extreme to the running of a very successful brewery, and chain of public houses, at the other. The latter was an arrangement which had remained in force ever since it had been made as an emergency measure during the First World War. Thereafter the senior civil servants responsible for such matters presumably subscribed to the dictum that "when it is not necessary to change, it is necessary not to change" and left things well alone. And so, for over half a century, the British Home Office offered a career to brewers and publicans in addition to those it extended to administrators and scientists. Unhappily the spectre of "rationalisation" finally caught up with the brewery and the pubs and they were sold off to private enterprise. Consequently, one of my secondary daydreams, that of being appointed head man in the pub and brewery department, disappeared to join the pile of jetsam already formed by so many of my other discarded fantasies.

The Home Office had made the first moves towards the setting up of an adequate laboratory service long before the Second World War with the foundation of the Metropolitan Police Forensic Science Laboratory and the taking under the Home Office wing of some smaller police laboratories. The advent of the war was not allowed to interrupt the process more than was absolutely necessary. During the early years of my service in the nineteen fifties the total of operational laboratories increased to eight and they served the whole of England and Wales. So these laboratories had been in existence for many years before the next logical step was taken by the setting up, in 1967, of the research facility already referred to and which I so desperately desired. Under the name of the "Home Office Central Research Establishment" this was where I was to serve a total of eight varied and very interesting years. The first two of these, as deputy to the director and as head of the Biology Division, saw us finding our conceptual feet and setting a pattern for research and investigation and of liaison with the operational laboratories. It was during this period that there crystallised in my mind the differences in approach between those scientists who were natural historians and those who were natural philosophers. This difference, I believe, is one that should always be kept in mind by anyone who works in the natural sciences, particularly in any applied field.

Nowadays the name "natural history" conjures up a vision of outdoor nature studies earnestly conducted by ladies in tweed suits and brogues (or latterly in anoraks and walking boots) and their disciples. It is a study which, although it has its scientific aspects, is considered not really to be a science in its own right. On the other hand the name "natural philosophy" currently stimulates little reaction from scientists because nowadays the name is barely known except as an archaic synonym for "physics" used only in the more ancient groves of academe. But both of these studies were originally equal partners in the field of "natural science" which itself was simply the study of natural phenomena. Yet even the name "natural science" has drifted in meaning for some of the newer educational institutions which have no anchor in the past. In these instances it is simply used as a synonym for "biology". So of what value is this discussion of names which were coined in more reflective times? Simply that they represent two complementary attitudes of mind to the study of nature of which all concerned with the applied sciences should be aware.

All studies of the natural world, including forensic science, depend on both observation and analysis. In natural history the observational aspect is predominant. In natural philosophy the analytical aspect prevails. The natural historian, including the crime investigator, tends to reason *a posteriori*, from effect to cause. He starts with the clues and hopes to reason his way to the criminal. He sorts through a medley of factual observations, carefully and without a prejudiced methodology.

Chapter Fourteen: Time to Think

He leaves any decisions on cause, and necessary consequent action, to a late stage in the process when he is quite sure he has absorbed all the relevant evidence, conflicting and disparate though it may be.

On the other hand the natural philosopher tends to be much more "scientific" in the modern sense of the word, when he views natural phenomena. He tends to work *a priori*, from within a framework of well established causes. He approaches phenomena more "objectively", using established scientific knowledge and theories as part of his universe of investigation. He is happiest with episodes which can be expressed with great precision, preferably mathematically. Neither of these approaches is the "right" one in all circumstances, they are two faces of the same investigative coin. But in the complex and unfamiliar situation it is best to adopt the more cautious method of the natural historian, until the situation crystallises to the stage where precise methods can be applied to the investigation of well defined phenomena. The situation is to some extent analogous to the comparison, elsewhere in this book, of crime investigation with the criminal trial. Crime investigation is a much more untidy business than the criminal trial mainly because it has little of the framework given by hindsight to the process of reasoning. My own taste and training was very much that of the natural historian, whereas that of my boss was essentially that of the natural philosopher. A very practical demonstration of this difference in our approach to investigation came early in my renewed research career.

My small unit was investigating the individuality of bloodstains. This is a perennial problem in forensic science and it has been approached in a number of different ways, some of which have already been touched upon in this book. The approach we were concerned with involved the patterns of soluble proteins which occur in the blood of human beings. This pattern varies and it is a variation of both kind and degree. Two individuals will differ to some extent because they diverge in the types of soluble protein in their bloods. They will also differ because individuals may possess some types of protein in common, yet differ in the amounts of each they have circulating in the blood.

The Sceptical Witness

The potential usefulness of such a situation lies in the possibility that bloodstains from crime scenes might be classifiable by means of their soluble proteins and so correlated with their sources. The barrier to developing this hope into a practical method lay in the fact that we had no suitable, practical method of analysis. Then one day we learned of a method invented by a medical researcher which might answer to our requirements. By using the electric charges which are present on the protein molecule surface, together with what are known as their "immunological" properties, we produced a picture visible to the naked eye, which reflected the amount and nature of the soluble proteins present in blood samples taken from different individuals.

The actual experimental procedure to obtain these results was somewhat complex but it doesn't concern us here. What does concern us is the nature of the pictures we obtained. These can best be described as a series of line drawings of mountain ranges individually of a remarkable complexity. Within any "mountain range" the individual peak was constituted by a single soluble protein. Each of these "line drawings" was experimentally produced on the glass plate of a standard projection slide. Because of this we were able to project the images on to a screen for detailed examination. We found that the picture for any single individual tended to remain constant and that it was usually easily discriminated from that of other individuals. So it looked as though the method might be of some forensic value. But there was a snag.

It was this. As the bloodstains aged the pattern for a single individual tended to change. An extract of a fresh bloodstain yielded a pattern just like that of the undried blood itself. Thereafter with the passage of time the pattern changed and, although some factors tended to remain constant, many altered. The visual evidence of this was that some protein peaks disappeared, and others reduced in size, with the passage of time. The question then was could we identify any factors which tended to be independent of bloodstain age?

Chapter Fourteen: Time to Think

Adopting the natural historian's approach I first mounted a series of preliminary experiments to see what degree of matching could be obtained simply by visual examination of the results, without any measurement or calculation. From these initial and rather crude experiments it seemed to me that some scientists were better at subjectively correlating bloodstains as being of the same origin than some of their colleagues were. It was simply a case of "I think that stain came from the same source as that blood sample". Obviously this ability could not be used as a scientific technique, but it occurred to me that if I could identify the factors that the successful classifiers were using then this might reduce the amount of work necessary to produce a fully objective technique. So I decided to approach the problem by a survey of as many scientists as were willing to participate in looking at pairs of plates and "guessing" the origins of the pairs as either from the same individual or not. It was a process in which I hoped to separate some useful experimental wheat from the observational chaff. If I could identify observers who were consistently good at correlating the samples accurately then there was a hope I might then be able to identify what factors they were unconsciously using. In this way much of the observational brushwood would be removed leaving a fairly clear experimental plain.

I set up a screen and two projectors and furnished the volunteer audience with questionnaires to complete as they observed successive pairs of pictures. First we embarked upon a briefing in which it was demonstrated how the pattern given by one individual differed from the pattern yielded by other individuals, using only fresh blood samples. Next we demonstrated how extracts of dried bloodstains gave the same pattern as the liquid bloods from which they were made provided that the bloodstains were fresh. Finally we demonstrated what happened to the patterns given by the bloodstains as they aged over a period of days. The sole question which was posed was "In the pair of images you observe do you feel it more likely that the two members of the pair are from one individual or from different individuals?

This carefully prepared survey came to nothing. The director, my boss, sitting on the back row of the theatre, made known his views that such a procedure was not science. This he did, I felt, by a method more appropriate to a dissatisfied audience member in a music hall than to a scientific forum. He was a man with a pithy turn of phrase and this added savour to the proceedings if not enlightenment to the scrutiny. The survey immediately folded, the audience broke up in hilarious disorder and the samples were returned to their boxes. My boss and I repaired to a private place where we each gave the other his frank opinion on the matter. His view, which under the circumstances was the only one that mattered, was that we must immediately put the problem out to external contract to highly mathematical specialists dealing with pattern recognition. This, remember, was in the days before the computer had taken up residence on the laboratory bench.

My own interest in the study waned as other topics attracted my attention and with the external contract under way I left the whole business to the "experts". I saw no reports on the study during the two years I spent as deputy at CRE but when, some six years later, I returned to CRE as director I asked for the report of the external contractor to be brought to me. There was none. All that existed was a few letters outlining progress, or rather lack of it, as the external contractors struggled to find an "objective" datum from which to start their comparisons. Doubtless they would have been better able to carry out their task had they been equipped, like contemporary scientists, with computer backup, but these were early days. It is possible that my own more intuitive initial study would have ended in exactly the same way with no clear experimental lines to follow. Perhaps the virtue of my method might simply have been that it was equally indeterminate, substantially quicker and very much cheaper.

My early service at CRE allowed me to make many friendships which have lasted over the years. It also gave me time to think without the looming background demands for scene examinations, case reports and court appearances. In addition it was the source of my view, although I didn't recognise it at the time, that research in applied science in general, and forensic science in particular, is better served from the outside inwards rather than the inside outwards. What do I mean by this? It is that when investigating a topic in applied science one is searching, by definition, for the empirical solution to an empirical problem. If the researcher is highly experienced in practical casework then he will intuitively know when a particular experimental approach is not the best one, given the practical constraints of casework. He will instinctively eliminate the impractical without, in many cases, consciously knowing that he is doing so. Conversely he will tend to recognise the positive features in any given experimental approach which might render it of value although this, I think, is a more difficult problem for him. The strength of using the experienced caseworker in research lies more in the recognition of irrelevant, if inviting, avenues rather than the identification of the best investigative path to follow.

The essence of investigating any problem is that the problem must be first defined in order for any study of it to be a success. If the investigator himself has faced the predicament before, under practical circumstances, then he is not under the same obligation to describe fully and explicitly what he means, as he would be were he describing the problem for others. Explicit verbal definition of a problem is an excellent tool for research, but the definition itself is a part of the caseworker's experience and he will recognise pitfalls which would have to be spelled out to the academic.

But sometimes a research study is embarked upon by an individual with no case work experience simply because he is highly qualified in an academic field which appears relevant to forensic science. This, at the time of which I am speaking, was fairly common because research appeared an unattractive option to casework for most competent forensic scientists. After all that was the only reason I got the research job myself as I described earlier. None of my colleagues wanted it.

One extremely interesting research topic which was well under way when I arrived at CRE was a method which was reputed to be able to characterise human head hair by means of its trace element content.

Supposedly unique to the individual, or nearly so, the pattern of trace elements in head hair was assessed by the use of Neutron Activation Analysis. The method required the use of an atomic pile, a facility which was available to us close by. A team of scientists, more or less loosely associated, worked on the problem. Nuclear physicists, chemists and mathematicians combined to seemingly confirm that the original finding, made in Canada, promised great advances in the characterisation of transfer traces.

But, with the passage of time, it became evident that the method was a forensic red herring, a fact which was confirmed some years later when the original researcher withdrew his "discovery". This was the mark of the honest researcher. Many would have simply allowed the sands of time to bury the matter in ambiguity. But at the time, unserved by the wisdom of hindsight, it seemed to us to be a very promising study.

A much more modest study related to the striations on finger nails. The reader may wish to participate in this by placing into juxtaposition, one by one and tip to tip, his left and right fingernails. Start with the pair of thumb nails and note the growth striations in the two nails. Do they match to any degree? Next try again with the pairs of index, middle, ring and little fingers. Now try the same thing again with your left hand and a friend's right hand and make your judgements. Extend the experimental design as much as necessary, carry out all the comparisons, write up your results and publish them. We never got to that stage, other things deflected us. What good might all this be? Well it did seem to us at the time that it might be of value in associating cognate fragments of bodies in post disaster investigations, aircraft crashes for example. At least we felt that it might be of practical, if only occasional, value. We could hardly involve ourselves in basic academic research with such a small staff as we had at that time, and we dearly wanted to be seen to be producing "useful" results.

But if one turns an experienced academic researcher loose in any field, applied or not, then publishable experimental results will begin to flow. However the applicable usefulness of such results will be a matter for the future after more research has been done rather than for the here and now. This not a sneer against academics, by a failed academic, but simply a description of what happens in practice. It may be pointed out with justice that the major recent advances in forensic science have all been based on fundamental university research. One could hardly have expected current practices in DNA characterisation, fingerprint recognition and sorting, and several other technology driven fields, without massive investment in university research. But it is a question of scale. The small applied research unit has little capacity to carry out basic research such as occurs in the university world. Its function is to adapt existing knowledge to its own concerns and to refine and improve the existing applied methods which it already uses.

A further job is to watch the progress of external research, in government, industry and the universities, and to decide when a particular line of inquiry has advanced to the stage where there is sufficient evidence that a project is an inevitable winner and would be speeded on the road to full practical application by patronage (the word was never used, or at least never written) from the potential users themselves. This aid could be financial in the shape of what we called an "external contract" in which we defined what we wanted and paid over money in the hope of getting it.

Some of our external contracts worked rather well. Others, (*vide supra*, the measurement of soluble proteins in blood) did not. But, successful or not, there was the perpetual problem of staying aware of what was going on in a study external to CRE but financed by us and appearing in our accounts. As in all fields of human involvement things tended to drift. What originally appeared to be a crystal clear definition of requirements, accepted by all parties, tended to become fogged by time. Left to their own devices external contractors tended to take primrose paths and drift into fields that, while scientifically fascinating, were not those defined by the contract.

The Sceptical Witness

The reasons and excuses for doing so were often quite convincingly expressed. "We are doing what you asked us to do but in a way we think is better than the original". Or "what we are doing is precisely what you asked us to do and it is you, not us, who have misunderstood". Or "This is our special field and we feel better qualified to decide than you" (comparatively unusual unless all moneys had already been paid over).

Some further examples will be given later in the book but for the moment we will turn to a lighter vein. After fifteen years during which my life had been ruled by the entirely unpredictable crime scene visit and the largely unpredictable requirements of the criminal courts, I suddenly found myself able to decide for myself what I would do and when I would do it.

One consequence of this was my decision to enter the field of amateur dramatics. This was something I never could have done when case working. Long term commitment to rehearsal and performance was hardly practicable in my hitherto uncertain world. But now things were different. I was master of my own free time. Shakespeare's tide in the affairs of men happened to surge at the same time. The local amateur dramatic society was putting on Fielding's "Tom Jones" and, a week before the performances were to start, one of the players withdrew from his role as the hangman. In a spirit of bravado, fuelled by good company and alcohol, I agreed to take the part. This was not a matter of design but simply a chance vacancy which I did not possess the wit, at the time, to avoid. The hangman had a non speaking part and only appeared on the stage for the final few minutes. This was the dramatic *dénouement* in which Tom, already on the scaffold with the noose around his neck, was rescued in the nick of time by the good Squire Western. The method of rescue was for the Squire to thrust open the doors at the back of the theatre, run down the aisle shouting "treachery, treachery!" and then to fire a musket ball accurately through the rope above Tom's head whereupon the halter would fall away. Happily the musket ball was an imaginary one. The apparent severing of the rope was effected by the hangman himself who pulled a concealed cord to make the halter fall. But even without the musket ball there were other hazards.

Firstly the scaffold was extremely narrow, a circumstance necessitated by the small size of the stage. On this narrow plank there were three characters in close proximity. These were the parson, Tom and the hangman. Even to get to this position where the final poignant moments of the tragedy were to be acted out there were obstacles to be surmounted. The first of these was my costume as the hangman. I wore a white shirt with lace ruffles at the neck and cuffs, black velvet breeches, white knee length socks and gold buckled black shoes. I felt myself to be a truly imposing sight and even began to think that, perhaps, I had missed my vocation. The trouble was the hood. This was made out of black cloth and had two holes for the eyes. It had been made for the previous player who, apparently, enjoyed little space between the top of his head and his eyes. This meant that when I pulled the hood on my eyes were well below the level of the eye holes. My request to the producer for a better fitting hood met with short shrift. Time was running out, it was only a week to opening night and he had more important things on his mind. I was advised, rather brusquely I thought, to pull the front of the hood down vigorously and then hold it in my teeth throughout the action. After all mine was a non-speaking part.

Rehearsals went quite well. When the final scene arrived we entered upstage right. Tom led the procession with his arms pinioned behind his back immediately followed by the priest reading from a prayer book. I followed last of all. The solemn cortège walked slowly downstage to the footlights where we turned and moved along the front of the stage before an awed and silent audience of drama club members. If the show were as realistic as the rehearsal then the real audience could not fail to be most impressed. The heat of the footlights penetrated under my ill-fitting hood and I began to sweat as we turned once again and headed back upstage to the scaffold. This was a rickety plank across the backdrop and it was reached by an equally rickety ladder. Tom climbed the ladder, the priest followed and, finally, so did

The Sceptical Witness

I. There wasn't much room. We edged along the scaffold to where the noose hung. The priest closed his prayer book and, with a final benediction committed Tom's soul to its destiny in the cosmos and edged his way back along the plank past me. This was in order to allow me to place the noose around Tom's neck. I kept the hood grimly fixed between my teeth as I edged along the scaffold, positioned the noose and groped for the concealed string which would allow me to "cut" the rope when the time came.

Silence reigned for a few seconds and then, spot on cue, the rear doors of the theatre flew open and Squire Western bounded in. "Treachery, treachery" he boomed as he sped down the aisle to the footlights. Up went his musket and BANG, down dropped the severed halter as, unseen by the audience, I sharply tugged the concealed cord. The crowd around the scaffold, largely female with fulsome bosoms cupped in eighteenth century bodices, bounced with joy. "Rescue, rescue!" they shrieked and then pelted me, the hated hangman, with rotten fruit. It was all most impressive and exciting.

The remainder of the rehearsals went well and, at the beginning of the following week, the show started. There were to be six evening performances from Monday to Saturday and although the audience was sparse on the Monday the rest of the week was a sell-out. It really was good for an amateur production. A colleague who saw it said how excellent it was and described how the hangman was an enormous and sinister figure in a black hood. I told him I played the part of the hangman and he refused to believe me, producing as proof a copy of the programme which still bore the name of the original hangman. "Anyway", said my colleague, " he was twice as big as you". So much for eye witness evidence.

It was a wonderful week. I got to know Squire Western quite well. In his periods off stage he would join me in the bar and talk to me of his interest in ancient firearms. He proudly displayed his musket to me. It was a replica of an eighteenth century original and it was most certainly a firearm within the meaning of the Act. He showed me how he

Chapter Fourteen: Time to Think

loaded it through the muzzle. First he poured in a charge of black powder and followed this with a wad of toilet paper which he packed down hard with a ramrod. The wad was a substantial one to ensure that pressure built up to make a realistic explosion. It was all quite safe he assured me, he was very experienced in its use. It certainly was a most impressive stage prop. The cast were in high spirits for the final performance of the week and there was just that hint of nervousness which goes with the knowledge of a job well done and one final hurdle to surmount. I could flatter myself I'd done pretty well. I'd kept the hood firmly in my teeth all week and I hadn't once fallen over the footlights or off the scaffold. My performance, like everyone else's, had been immaculate. It now remained merely to ice a most successful cake.

The final show began well. No-one missed his cue or fluffed his lines. Squire Western joined me in the bar in his off stage intervals, a perfect replica of how Fielding must have imagined his original in tricorn hat, tailed coat and riding boots. He charged his gun generously with black powder and toilet paper. "Give 'em a good bang for their money on the last night" he said ramming in an extra charge of black powder and a supplementary length of toilet paper. Finally he primed the gun with a percussion cap, wished me luck and went to his spot at the back of the theatre. I joined Tom and the priest in the wings. Silence fell on the auditorium as the awesome procession appeared. The pathetic yet defiant hero, followed by the ministering priest and, finally, by the menacing figure of the hangman. We advanced slowly along our now well practised route and I felt the heat of the footlights penetrating under the ill-fitting hood as I clenched it firmly between my teeth to hold the eye holes in position, determined that nothing should go wrong on the last night. We turned back up the stage and then up the scaffold steps. Up on to the scaffold and across the backdrop we went in utter silence save for the voice of the priest.

We reached the halter, stopped, and the priest closed his prayer book with a final benediction for Tom's eternal soul. Then he wormed past me and I took up my place next to Tom. I placed the noose around his neck, grasped the hidden cord and awaited the final thespian triumph of the week. The wait seemed eternal. At the back of the auditorium Squire Western stood with his musket cocked, squinting through the crack in the swing doors as he followed the scene on the stage. He waited until he judged the perfect moment had arrived then kicked the doors open and, with a triumphant whoop, rushed into the theatre, tripped, and pulled the trigger.

WHOOMPH! went the gun. It was quite definitely a WHOOMPH rather than a BANG because of the superabundance of black powder and toilet paper that the squire had inserted into the barrel. The members of the audience were terrified out of their wits. One moment they were watching a muted and tragic scene on the stage and the next there was this enormous blast at the back of the theatre. The poor devils must have thought the day of judgement had come.

The silence that followed seemed eternal as I stood irresolutely on the scaffold behind Tom while a golden rain of incandescent toilet paper settled gently and quietly on to the heads of the audience. I hadn't the faintest idea of what to do. If I pulled the string the audience wouldn't know why the halter had fallen away. If I didn't pull it we would all be there till doomsday. I was just about to pull it, on the basis that the audience was in no fit state to reason anything out anyway, when something happened. Squire Western, now badly bruised, had got to his feet and was limping agonisingly down the aisle dragging his discharged and useless musket behind him as he muttered "Treachery, treachery!" He reached the footlights and painfully lifted the gun to his shoulder and, with all the drama he could muster, he said "BANG!" Thankfully I pulled the string and the halter dropped away. All the bosoms bounced as the girls shrieked "Rescue, rescue!" and pelted me, the hangman, with rotten fruit. Then the audience pieced it all together and, as Squire Western painfully climbed on to the stage, he was given a hero's welcome.

Chapter Fourteen: Time to Think

It was Squire Western's night and he received great applause at the curtain calls as the man who had snatched success from the jaws of failure so bravely. I even received an appreciative cheer myself but, in that moment, I decided that a life in the theatre was not for me. I preferred the comparatively tranquil life of the murder scene, the laboratory and the witness box, and to these we shall now return.

The Sceptical Witness

Chapter Fifteen: Hinnies and Lonnens

I was in Toronto when the news came through to me that I had been promoted to the directorship of my own laboratory. As deputy at the Central Research Establishment I had travelled to Canada with my boss to give several scientific papers at an international conference on forensic science. Most of the papers were not my own. This was because there was only limited financial backing for attendance at the meeting and I had exercised naked privilege to ensure that one of the only two airline tickets available went to me. As a quid pro quo for the exercise of this *droit de seigneur adjoint* I agreed to present the papers of those who had to stay behind in the laboratory and so could not give them themselves. One must encourage the young.

Giving other peoples papers is a very good education for those whose job regularly includes explaining technical subjects to non technical audiences. It is very necessary to concentrate on the essential issues involved, to understand them as far as possible, to anticipate any possible questions and prepare answers to them in advance. It is also sometimes a good idea to leave enough flexibility in the text to be able to lengthen it where necessary so as to fill all the time available with the presentation itself and thus avoid questions altogether.

Leaving Toronto for the moment and digressing instantly to Paris I remember another conference I attended in which the same duty, reading papers outside my specialty, fell to me. Communication at the meeting was blunted to some extent by the fact that there was simultaneous interpretation into four languages, and this doubtless obstructed the posing of penetrating questions by specialists in the audience. As one American author shrewdly remarked "working through an interpreter is like hacking your way through the jungle with a feather"

Nevertheless I was rather thankful when I had finished reading one of the papers in my collection because not only was I largely ignorant of the subject involved but I found it profoundly boring, and so hadn't prepared it as well as I should have done. After giving the paper and regaining my seat next to a colleague he leaned over and whispered quietly in my ear "Stuart, I know no-one else who can speak at such

length, and so convincingly, on a subject of which he knows nothing".
I felt rather pleased.

It was at this same conference that I was dealing with a questions
session from the rostrum when I had another rewarding experience.
The audience consisted, as it always did in this organisation, of representatives
from perhaps thirty or forty different countries speaking
one of the four conference official languages, English, French, German
or Spanish. Many of the delegates were anxious that they should
be seen to have been active during the conference and, to this end,
they asked questions simply to have their names and the questions and
responses inscribed into the written record. This was important because
it was the basis upon which they would be judged when they got
back home and the meeting report fell into the boss's in-tray.

One of the questioners was a diminutive man from one of France's
former African colonies. He spoke in heavily accented French and he
was very, very nervous. His nervousness communicated itself to everyone
else in the audience and so back to the questioner himself. As he
struggled with the problem of a too complicated question a minority
of the audience began to mutter impatiently and the interpreters gave
up trying to make sense of what he said. After several minutes of this,
which seemed like hours to everyone else, and in an obvious state of
abject misery he finally sat down in his seat and stared wretchedly at
the floor. The audience was deathly silent. Suddenly, standing there
on the rostrum, I suffered a time slip, as I so often do, and I was back
at the municipal banquet in Yorkshire where, unprepared, I was thrust
into making a speech when I'd never made one before. I knew exactly
how the poor devil felt. At least I had been on my home ground when
it happened to me and the consequences of my performance would
not have impinged on my future career. But he was in a foreign country
trying to hold his own with a largely sophisticated and unsympathetic
gathering whose contempt was beginning to show.

Chapter Fifteen: Hinnies and Lonnens

I gathered my papers together, as if in deep thought and leaned forward to the rostrum microphone, and began to speak. "The speaker" I said "has touched upon a very important question and I am most grateful to him for having given me the opportunity of dealing with the matter". Whilst I was speaking my mind raced as I tried to correlate a few of the questioner's hesitant words with the content of the paper I had just given. Then I continued "As I see it the essence of the question is...." and here I posed a question such as might have been asked under other and better organised circumstances. I spoke slowly and distinctly to give the interpreters and minute takers no excuse for error as my question wended its tortuous way through the electronic equipment, then through the minds of the interpreters and finally on to the paper which was destined to fall into the in-tray of the little man's boss. Then, equally slowly and distinctly, I gave the answer to my own question. It was evident that the audience was completely taken in by the stratagem, and perhaps I even convinced the questioner himself that he had performed well. But whatever the truth of the matter I finished my presentation, gathered up my papers and turned to leave the rostrum.

The chairman of the session was the secretary general of the international organisation that had arranged the conference. He was multilingual, highly sophisticated and very experienced in the ways of international verbal exchange. I walked behind his chair to leave the rostrum and he caught hold of my arm. I bent to listen to what he had to say. "Mr Kind", he said in fluent and slightly accented English, "you have missed your vocation. You should have been a diplomat". That was the only time in my life that anyone has implied that I could be diplomatic.

I have always felt that the value of scientific conferences is rather debatable, but I have taken great care not to flaunt this view whenever there was a chance of going to one myself. After all, they usually proved to be very enjoyable social occasions, and one could always point to useful discussions with opposite numbers from other countries as a justification for participation. But the most efficient method for the dissemination of scientific knowledge is the printed word with perhaps a good lecturer coming second. The best vehicle for the dissemination of practical expertise is apprenticeship under an expert in a well established institution. After these two requirements have been met the conference can provide a useful appendix but it cannot replace the first two. One supposes that the advent of teleconferencing might reduce the need for international seminars. If the supposition is correct there is certainly no evidence for it as far as this retired scientist can see at the time of writing.

But back to the conference in Toronto. With typical arrogance I had assumed I would get the vacant job of laboratory director over more senior people. After all I was totally convinced I was the best man (sorry "person") for the job, but it still came as a pleasure when the decision was made and the news came through to the Toronto conference that I was the new director of the Home Office Northern Regional Laboratory. At last I was commander of my own independent unit. Somewhat later, after my return to England, there was a sudden deflation to my ego when I learned that the post had first been offered to a more senior scientist who had refused it on the grounds that he was perfectly content as he was and where he was. Oh so happy those without ambition.

My arrival as director of the Northern Region Forensic Science Laboratory was a red letter day for me. Situated just north of Newcastle upon Tyne the laboratory was set in a very distinctive locality peopled by very characteristic inhabitants. Centuries of border warfare against the marauding Scots, and the exercise of their own marauding techniques over the border into Scotland, had left its stamp upon the local society. Those who believe the West was wild should read the history of warfare on the English Scottish frontier whereupon they would tend to classify the Wild West along with tea parties at an English vicarage. The region was perhaps a little backward in the matters of refined personal manners and elegant social niceties, but it was a model in matters of kindness and helpfulness to one's neighbours. I soon became used to being addressed as "hinny", a title that was used universally without regard to any social status real or imagined. Place names were distinctive too. One might drive down Two Ball Lonnen on the way to Kitty Brewster or Pity Me. The people and places were kindly, lovely, and untidily distinctive.

The region had suffered by its distance from London as remote towns so often do, in any country, when a long way from the capital. It was during my stay as director of the Newcastle laboratory that I learned how deeply uninformed our rulers, in the cockpits of power in London, could be regarding the geography of their own country. The incident in question took place after I had been in post at Newcastle for several years. At this time I had already developed the firm opinion that the sleeping dogs of top management should be left to lie as long as possible without disturbance. Unhappily there arose a question which required the guidance of my masters in London for its solution. It was with reluctance that I picked up the telephone and spoke to head office.

With the smoothness that is a uniform characteristic of those classically educated at the ancient universities of England, and with the aplomb shown by all those confident in their right to rule, the mandarin on the other end of the line listened to me patiently. He finally agreed that my problem was a knotty one and should not be subject to an *ad hoc* solution on the spot. However, although he could not solve the problem himself, he would pass me through to someone who could. There followed a series of conversations with individuals each of whom denied that the problem fell within his purlieu and passed me on to the next. Finally I was returned to the mandarin to whom I first spoke. His discomfiture at not knowing the solution to my dilemma began to show but suddenly a relieved tone of triumph came into his voice. "Where did you say you were speaking from?" he asked. "Newcastle upon Tyne" I replied. "Oh, you don't want us" he said in the manner of a schoolmaster addressing a less than acute pupil. "You want the Scottish Office. That's in Edinburgh". At that point I gave up and made the decision myself.

The Sceptical Witness

My arrival at the laboratory as the new director had a pleasure all its own. I was shown to my office and then walked around the laboratory and introduced myself to the staff. In most cases this was not necessary because I already knew most of them and some were old workmates of mine, an added circumstance which lent flavour to the occasion. Preliminaries over I returned to the director's office and called in the senior staff. For the rest of the morning I outlined my philosophy of management and quizzed each one in turn on his views relating to all aspects of laboratory affairs. I enjoyed myself so much that I did not noticed the passage of time until one hungry person suggested that if we didn't break up the meeting pretty quickly we wouldn't get any lunch.

Because the laboratory was located on a government site along with several other ministries we shared a canteen with them and it was to this that we quickly repaired. My new staff respectfully allowed me to lead the way to the servery where it became evident that several dishes were no longer on the menu. Not wishing to order something no longer available I asked the lady at the servery what remained on the menu? She answered me at length, patiently describing the several dishes still obtainable. My inadequacies as the new director became immediately apparent because I did not understand a word she said. No, that is not quite true. From the extended culinary disquisition in the vernacular I managed to recognise a single dish, cold chicken. So I had the cold chicken. I was too embarrassed to ask for a translation of the rest of the menu.

This did not augur well for my stay in Newcastle. If I couldn't understand the natives I would not fit in very well. I could hardly proceed about my daily business with an interpreter. Happily I had inherited a highly intelligent secretary, a local lady, who took it upon herself to educate me in the regional dialect. With the passage of time we even used to converse in it, much to the amusement of the other staff. But I was never totally happy with the local language unlike my wife, a Londoner, who adapted fully and immediately to the linguistic demands. We obviously heard the sounds differently.

Chapter Fifteen: Hinnies and Lonnens

Why should this be? It was not lack of empathy on my part, or willingness to learn. After all I was able to mimic several British regional accents in a passable way so I grasped how variable phonetics could be. From time to time I even scored some minor successes in naming the regions of origin of various speakers of English so I had, to some extent, the ability to distinguish accent. Perhaps it was the onset of progressive deafness, the "Lancaster Ear" which stemmed from sharing a small space with four unsilenced Rolls Royce Merlin engines that gave me the problem. But I doubt if this could be the entire story.

My embarrassment was somewhat lessened by an incident in which one of my staff went to the scene of a suspicious fire in a local working men's club. When he came back he looked noticeably strained and I asked him what was the matter. He told me that he had spent several hours with the club secretary and had not understood a single word the secretary uttered during this time. This was remarkable because the scientist himself was a northerner although from the northwest of England rather than the northeast. I comforted myself that at least I was not alone with my disability.

Some years later I accepted a part time academic appointment which required me to travel to Glasgow in Scotland from time to time. Much the same thing happened again, and I was forced to give up travelling by air because of my embarrassment at journeying from the airport into town and not being able to respond intelligently to the questions of the voluble and friendly taxi drivers. Instead I travelled by rail via Edinburgh, a longer journey but with no loquacious taxi drivers involved.

Phoneticians are aware of how distinctively individual the human voice can be. Not only is there the general matrix of regional accent but superimposed upon this is the personal imprint of the individual speaker, perhaps not as distinctive as fingerprints but of a highly informative nature as many police investigators can testify. I recall an early experience in a Yorkshire assize court where, after conversing with the investigating officer in the case for some time, he asked me what year I had left Nottingham? This despite the fact that I had, at that stage, given him no indication of my origins.

Nowadays there is a separate study of forensic phonetics, and police investigators are aware of the value they can sometimes draw from consultation with these experts. In the Yorkshire Ripper investigation one hoax tape recording was ascribed to a particular district of Sunderland near Tyneside, and the entire investigation was distorted thereafter. This was simply a wrong operational decision made by the chief investigating officer. The phonetics were faultless.

But phonetics and other digressions apart I now had a new laboratory to run and I was determined that any mistakes which occurred in that employment would be my own. I would listen to all relevant advice as carefully as possible and then make up my own mind. In the way of all new brooms I swept clean, at least as I thought, although this was welcomed by some and opposed by others. All organisations can benefit from a change of management from time to time. The problem is to agree upon what is the ideal time for change and we can be sure that humanity will never agree on this score. One of my senior assistants was a man I knew very well, with whom I had worked before and whom I personally liked very much. The trouble was that his section was quite disorganised in matters of arrangement of equipment and records. Put less kindly it was a tip which had been allowed to accrue for years by the previous management who had failed to come to adequate grips with a highly distinctive section head. This manager was quite determined that he would continue to have his own way with me too and the matter dragged on for some time until one day when it had really become an issue. Happily he played into my hands when, before his own section staff, he responded to my request that he saw to the matter immediately. In an unmistakeably adversarial manner, and with the faintest hint of insolence in his voice, he said "is that an order?" All I had to do was to reply "yes" and the matter was resolved. Presumably my predecessor would have been more reasonable.

Chapter Fifteen: Hinnies and Lonnens

Any organisation must have a structure and it must have rules. Were this not so it would not be recognisable as an organisation. The perennial problem is to decide how much of the function of the laboratory should exist in the form of clearly defined rules, and how much in the form of patterns of work which have simply evolved through practice. Too many rules leads to the suppression of initiative, too few leads to a variable performance of staff members as each works according to his own ideas. The more expert an individual is the more he can be expected to use optimum procedures and to produce accurate and informative results. The less expert he is (for whatever reason) the more he requires the defined procedure. The best would seem to be the application of the minimum of rules which can be imposed upon the whole of the work force. This avoids the generation of resentment by the exercise of different amounts and types of restrictions to members of a group who consider themselves of equal status.

And there is always the question of drift. No matter how carefully a laboratory system is defined, once it is working one can expect that its pattern will evolve with the passage of time and not always to the benefit of the laboratory. Each of us possesses an element of knowing what is best irrespective of any rules. Consequently the processes of forgetting, bending and breaking precepts are ever present in any work patterns. The product becomes variable dependent upon the particular producer involved. Rules may be produced as "guidelines". These are principles which should be adhered to unless there is good reason to the contrary. As an educational instrument they are unexceptionable. As an operational tool they are highly questionable. Where one is required to take action in a developing situation there is always the temptation to pay too much regard to "guidelines" because of the fear of what might appear at any *post facto* analysis of how a problem has been approached. The argument that one has followed the guidelines is a powerful excuse for failure.

But in laboratory work one is seldom faced with the same problems as an investigating officer in a murder case, or in a police stand off with a gunman. Laboratory tasks are usually more routine than these although any explicit admission of this should be made with caution lest the unusual features of a case remain unnoticed by those whose minds work in routine channels.

The atmosphere on my arrival at the laboratory was a good one. I had inherited a generally efficient and happy organisation for which I was duly thankful but it was a laboratory of individuals, of independent investigators each of whom ruled his own small kingdom. I was determined to amalgamate the kingdoms. I introduced two new sets of rules in my new laboratory. One of these related to the chemical analysis of urine and blood for alcohol content. The other was concerned with the monitoring of the throughput of case work in the laboratory.

Taking the analytical problem first I noticed that, in common with most laboratories of the time, the reporting of blood and urine alcohol levels was left to the individual analyst. These, usually very experienced, scientists were left to decide which analytical figure represented the most accurate for reporting purposes. When one is analysing a difference of degree, a quantitative difference, there is always some variation in the figures one obtains from repeat analyses. The more experienced the analyst the less the variation but it is nevertheless always there. The idea that there is a single entirely accurate figure is a fallacy, at least under practical circumstances, despite what the philosophers might tell us.

But this variation is no reason to allow analytical anarchy to reign and this was largely the situation I found. The criteria used by different analysts for reporting their findings differed and my modest contribution was simply to define a series of criteria, an algorithm as it is sometimes called, which established a uniform procedure which ensured that certain minimum tests were applied to all the analytical results. The technical details are unimportant here except to say that they allowed easy checking when, as was my habit, I monitored a variety of cases which passed through the laboratory.

Chapter Fifteen: Hinnies and Lonnens

There was marked opposition to the introduction of the new system as there always is when new rules are imposed upon well established routines. Nevertheless the scheme became an integral part of laboratory life. Some ten years later, after the laboratory had been amalgamated with another to form a much larger unit I happened to become the director of this combined laboratory. I noted with pleasure that my algorithm had been adopted for use in the unified laboratory. Although it was slightly battered in detail by the passage of the years it was still my original intellectual baby. Of course my signature had been removed. All this will seem very strange to the modern forensic scientist who is used to working in a much more advanced, specialised and defined framework, but those were pioneer days.

The second set of rules I introduced related to the recording of case throughput in the laboratory. One highly colourful member of my staff was known to boast that he had the oldest unreported case of any forensic science laboratory in the United Kingdom. This was one of the factors which made me decide to monitor more closely just how long the different types of case took to pass through the laboratory. To do this I instructed that the time lapse in reporting individual cases in the laboratory should be recorded so that I had a management tool to help me to assess performance and to determine trends. This was an easy thing to do. I simply ordered that, for each case, the date of receipt should be subtracted from the date of the final report and the result, mathematical and philosophical niceties apart, was the number of whole days the examination had taken.

It was quickly pointed out to me that cases reported on the day of receipt would show a zero time. Furthermore, because the laboratory only worked a five-day week in routine cases then it was "unfair" that the weekends should be included in the time lapse. I insisted that the rule remained in its pristine form. It was simple to apply, crime didn't stop at weekends and it was, after all, only a management tool and we each knew its shortcomings.

The Sceptical Witness

At the end of its first year of application the "time lapse in reporting cases" featured in my director's annual report and was viewed with disfavour by my fellow directors whose own annual reports contained no such breast-baring features. During the subsequent years the recorded time lapses in reporting cases in my laboratory showed a steady improvement and I was able to point to the effectiveness of this idea in monitoring case throughput. Unhappily one factor missed my attention. Although the rule how to calculate the time lapse was defined clearly and simply it was applied by several different human beings in the laboratory office dependent upon who was available at the time.

Each retained the instinctive view that it was "unfair" to include the weekends in the calculation and, as time passed, each began, at different times, to leave the weekends out of the calculation. And so the apparent improvement in laboratory performance was largely a result of a drift in reporting methods. By the time I noticed this illegitimate practice there was a substantial number of fallacious "time lapses" in the system. However they were too extensive to go back and correct, considering the amount of current case-work we had. So I simply left them as they were and made sure that, thereafter, everyone followed the official method. Did I comment on the error in a subsequent annual report? No I did not. Everyone knows there are lies, damned lies, and statistics.

After this error I sometimes used to imagine the ghost of the great French chemist, Henry Louis Chatelier, drifting around my laboratory with an amused smile on his spectral face. It was he who, in 1888, enunciated the principle which has since formed a part of the education of all chemists.

If a system is in stable equilibrium and one of the conditions is changed then the equilibrium will shift in such a way as to tend to restore the original condition.

He said this in relation to chemical reactions but it obviously applies to human organisations too.

Chapter Fifteen: Hinnies and Lonnens

I share with all forensic scientists of substantial casework experience a profound knowledge of the difference between *a priori* (cause to effect) reasoning and *a posteriori* (effect to cause) reasoning. The knowledge is instinctual because such terms are not nowadays the subject of teaching in our scientific schools. Perhaps the modern scientist is no worse off for that but I doubt it, and I cling to my belief that there are two distinct but interlocking facets of the process of "heuristic", or "how we find out". The antipathy of many scientists towards what they refer to as "philosophy" if they are kindly disposed, or "metaphysics" if they are not, is well illustrated by the following incident.

I had the job of chairing a session of several papers at a scientific meeting and I was sitting on the rostrum with the first speaker as the audience filed in, in the usual desultory fashion of those who have just had a good lunch. Whilst they were settling down in their seats and the latecomers were joining them, I passed the time chatting to the first speaker. His subject was "Forensic Science, Past, Present and Future". "Did he intend" I asked "to define his terms before starting the lecture? After all, there was a continuous flow of time and the three properties on his title merged one into the other with no perceptible physical boundary". I continued in this amiable and humorous strain (as I thought) until I glanced at my first speaker's face and saw that it was as black as thunder. I stopped and he snarled (no other verb would be equally fitting) that he certainly would not be indulging in such non-scientific rubbish.

The atmosphere between us, for the rest of his participation, was icy. But his reaction, admittedly less emphatic, would probably have been that of most of my scientist colleagues and perhaps they are all right. But I shall persist in thinking that they are not. Such questions are closely allied to that most practical of problems, the treatment of information in crime investigation. There are two interlocking aspects of this and all investigators, including all forensic scientists, should be constantly and consciously aware of the difference. It is the difference between assembling a pattern, or *a posteriori* reasoning, and reviewing a pattern, or *a priori* reasoning. It is the difference between the criminal investigation and the criminal trial. It is the difference between reasoning from the particular to the general and the reasoning from the general to the particular. In some aspects, although I would not push the analogy too far, it is the difference between foresight and hindsight.

A case history here would illustrate this to some extent. One day a blood sample arrived at the laboratory in a case of driving whilst over the statutory level of alcohol in the bloodstream. We received many hundreds of these cases each year and this one appeared unremarkable. The analyst examined the sample and found that there was no alcohol present. He then reported his findings and passed on to his other cases. Some time later the police officer in the affair rang the laboratory and asked if there could have been a mistake. When arrested the defendant, who smelt greatly of alcohol, admitted to having consumed a large amount of liquor. Was it not remarkable that the lab had found none? The analyst went back and checked the sample again. There was no mistake. The blood was devoid of alcohol. So if what the police officer said was true then it was quite remarkable that the lab had found no alcohol in the blood.

It transpired that there was a way of checking if there had been confusion with the samples somewhere along the line because another sample of the defendant's blood was available. This was because of the legal requirement that a sample of blood taken for alcohol determination be divided into two and one half offered to the defendant. This had been done but the defendant refused to take his sample and it was still available at the police station.

The second sample was duly sent into the lab and on analysis was found to contain a substantial level of alcohol. There were two other factors of difference. The label on each sample was written in a different hand and the two blood samples came from different persons as grouping tests showed. It became evident that the first sample which came into the lab was a substitute for the genuine one which was no longer traceable. Furthermore it was obvious that the individual who had rung the changes was a police officer, but the question was which one?

As was the usual practice in such cases a detective from another police force was called in to investigate the matter. Over the weeks of his investigation nothing transpired which pointed to the offender and it seemed that the mystery would never be solved. Then one day we were discussing the case over a coffee break in the lab and a staff member suggested a new method of approach. If the individual who falsified the sample and label was a police officer then it was at least possible that there were some genuine samples still in the laboratory which he had submitted in the normal course of events and which would bear his handwriting. If one of these could be found then the sample falsifier would be identified.

I thought this was an extremely shrewd suggestion and wondered why no-one had thought of it before. I wondered even more when it transpired that a matching label had been found in the lab store and the offender identified. So, with the wisdom conferred by hindsight, it was evident that we "should have" thought about it before we did. Not that "we" thought about it at all. The idea had occurred to only one staff member and, I recollect, it was not very well received by his colleagues at the time as likely to yield a result. So now that we knew the result it was obvious that we "should have" carried out the examination of the stock of old sample labels before we did. But it was not at all obvious at the time and it required the bright illumination of hindsight to demonstrate to us what an obvious investigatory path it was. When the "truth" has been exposed then things seem to fit in very easily and this is a factor which should be constantly in the mind of anyone charged with the reviewing of any investigation.

As a rule I never concerned myself with the human side of cases, feeling that the science and management involved was more than enough to keep me well occupied. My curiosity got the better of me in this case however and I made enquiries. The story revealed was rather sad. The person who had given the sample of blood was a local tradesman who needed his driving licence to continue in his job. He had given the two samples of blood in the normal way and the police officer in the case left them at the police station. One was meant for transmission to the laboratory and the other was the defendant's sample which he had refused to take away with him. A police sergeant in the station knew the defendant and was aware that he had a handicapped child and that loss of his job would be a major disaster. Humanly, but most unwisely, the sergeant took a sample of his own alcohol free blood, labelled it with the name of the defendant and despatched it to the laboratory Then he discarded the genuine sample. His downfall was the fact that he didn't discard the other sample too. Next by putting his own undisguised handwriting on the label, together with the fact that he regularly despatched genuine samples to the laboratory, he finally sealed his fate. In committing this act, with the best of intentions, he ruined his own career. He was charged with, and convicted of, "conspiring to pervert the course of justice" and was dismissed from the force.

After three or four years in charge of my lab I began to think that the time had come to move on. The problem was that I was a member of a comparatively small service and it was a question of waiting for suitable vacancies to occur and this did not happen very often. I had often thought that, given the opportunity, I would have made a good crime investigator in a wider and more general field than forensic science itself. This was a time of amalgamations and rethinking of roles and structures amongst the police forces of England and Wales, and so I was not surprised one day to see an advertisement for the chief constable's job of one of the larger northern forces. The advertisement did not specify that the applicant should be a police officer and I began to think of applying for the job myself. I rang the clerk to the police authority concerned and he confirmed that it was not necessary for an applicant to be a police officer. A long conversation terminated by the clerk saying they would be pleased to receive an application from me. There was however a snag. Although the police authority could make an appointment to a chief constable's post it did not become effective until it had been confirmed by higher authority. And the higher authority? None other than my own employers, the Home Office.

I saw no future in going through all the procedure of application, interview and possible appointment if the final result was going to be a refusal to ratify my appointment, so I made suitable enquiries through my headquarters. At this time we were fortunate enough to have a lady administrator with a special responsibility for the Forensic Science Service. She was a shrewd, very able and self possessed person, but even she could not entirely disguise the surprise in her voice when I described my intended course of action. The idea of a non police officer being appointed to a chief's job was one which had not been entertained since before the Second World War.

I posed the question "If I applied for the job and was successful would it be likely that the Home Office would confirm the appointment"? I did not expect any "official" view of the matter considering the necessity for the department not to be seen interfering in the business of local appointments made by committee. Presumably the necessity for confirmation of chief constable appointments was a central governmental power retained in order to ensure that lunatics and other undesirables were not chosen for such important jobs. So all I asked for was an unofficial indication of what might happen should I be chosen for the job. She promised to enquire amongst the highest echelons of management. This she did and shortly afterwards she telephoned me back. The answer was short and to the point. "Your appointment would not be confirmed" she said. And so I was grouped with the lunatics and other undesirables. I can't recollect feeling upset.

Some days later the clerk to the police authority rang me and asked me where my application was. I told him I had changed my mind but did not give the reason. There was no use stirring up a hornets' nest with no possible advantage to myself. Since that time I have often thought about the matter and have come to the conclusion that the Home Office was perfectly right in its view. There is absolutely no evidence that an outside appointment from non police officers would be a success. The perennial view that there should be an independently appointed officer class in the police has no justification in the real world. In those comparatively few cases where it has occurred, such as a short-lived scheme from just before the war, there is no evidence that the appointees consistently did any better than others who came up through the ranks. I have personally known two of "Lord Trenchard's young men" who were appointed directly as officers without a period on the beat. One was very good in his own way, highly regarded by his men but incautious to a degree. The other was a disaster.

All appointments to the police should be through the ranks. All appointments to the police should require substantial beat experience because dealing with the public is the essence of police work including crime investigation. Certainly police officers should be as well educated as possible but this does not mean that an academic record is *per se* a qualification for the job. The fact that assorted journalists, academics and politicians may hold other views is of comparatively little importance. In this respect they should all be classified with lunatics, other undesirables and upstart forensic scientists.

So I pleasantly soldiered on in my post feeling thankful all the time that fate had placed me to work amongst intelligent and educated people in a pleasant environment on projects which were unequivocally to the advantage of society. No-one can dispute that the effectiveness of the investigation of crime and of the criminal trial depends upon the existence of reliable factual information and that was what we were there to uncover.

I still maintained my interest in research matters although there was little time to devote to this in a very busy operational laboratory. We were able to produce several small pieces of applied research which added to the sum total of forensic science knowledge. One of these related to the use of "tagging powders". These substances are manufactured by forensic science laboratories and used to detect contact of individuals with particular locations or objects. Such tagging powders have been used for many years, certainly from before I became a forensic scientist, and they worked as follows.

Chapter Fifteen: Hinnies and Lonnens

If I place a distinctive, but not obvious, substance in a particular spot and subsequently find a trace of that substance on the hands or clothing of a suspect this might be taken as evidence that he had been in that spot or touched that particular object. Obviously questions could arise of secondary transfer from a criminal to an innocent person but careful design of the transfer conditions can help negate such questions. The question is how does one decide if the transferred material comes from the labelled spot and not from some other source? Traditionally this problem has been solved by forensic scientists making up their own recipes.

For example, if the police wished to tag a certain spot where chronic pilfering had been occurring in a factory then the laboratory could provide them with a tag to use in the form of a distinctive powder in a greasy base. Usually such tags also contained a fluorescent compound so that, under an ultraviolet lamp, the material gave off a coloured fluorescence. Imagine then a series of possible culprits from the factory staff lining up to have their hands examined under ultraviolet light. The one who shows a positive fluorescence is examined further and the scientist is able to state that the fluorescence is generated by a particular tag that he manufactured and supplied to the police at such and such a time.

The constitution of the tags were very much *ad hoc*, rather like favourite kitchen recipes. Faced with the problem of manufacturing a tag one scientist might choose a petroleum jelly base, put in some anthracene powder as a fluorescent agent, add some rice starch and a little oak sawdust. The result would be highly distinctive under the microscope and easily recognisable by the scientist who made the substance. Furthermore it would be difficult to imagine that someone else had made the same mixture for whatever purpose, or that it might occur somewhere in nature. In practice the appearance of a brightly fluorescent stain on a suspect's hands was often enough to cause confession on the spot.

The Sceptical Witness

These tagging cases were a very minor part of the work of the lab but I often thought that if such powders were available to the police and laboratory service in millions of different types, each identifiable by any experienced forensic scientist and classifiable on a nationally known scale, then they might become more widely used in the field of crime investigation. It is a fascinating study for thought experiments but I will leave those to the reader and pass on to my idea of how to solve the practical issues. This I did by taking Lycopodium powder, anciently listed in pharmacopoeias and still freely available in commerce. Under the microscope these very uniformly sized spores have a distinctive shape and can be easily spotted. Furthermore I found that they could be dyed in a range of brilliant colours making them even simpler to locate in microscopical amount. And so, by mixing the different, singly coloured, lycopodium spores in different ratios I had my almost unlimited range of tagging powders. My enthusiasm for the project was unlimited. That of my employers and most of my colleagues was non-existent.

Nevertheless I went ahead with the project with the help of some able assistants. With visions of future fortunes to be made I personally wrote a patent which still graces my study wall as I write, and then awaited success and riches. Twenty five years later I am still waiting. The powders were never generally used for the purpose for which they were meant although several intriguing spin-off applications were found. Perhaps in some more modern form such materials will one day be used widely in crime investigation. One can imagine microscopic bar coded chips and automatic pattern recognition in place of coloured spores and microscopy. I think it is likely that some such systems are already in use for purposes which the discerning reader will immediately recognise. But one does not bring such topics into the field of public debate.

With my time at the Newcastle laboratory completed I was appointed to the Directorship of the Central Research Establishment at Aldermaston to take over from my erstwhile boss who himself had moved to the top position of Controller of the Forensic Science Serv-

Chapter Fifteen: Hinnies and Lonnens

ice. And so the natural historian took over from the natural philosopher with its inevitable differences of approach to research. But it was an easy move for me to make having already served as deputy and being able to move into the lead position of an organisation which my predecessor had made the foremost organisation of its kind in the world. I didn't envy him in his new job. He moved from being the biggest fish in a small but very high quality pool, to being a medium sized one in a huge and rather amorphous government organisation. I wished him well and settled into the comfortable chair which he had left me.

It was paradise. There can be nothing better for those individuals who are fascinated by the process of heuristic, of "finding out", than to be the head of an organisation of people chosen largely on the basis of their intellects. Each working day was a process of discovery, a joyful exchange of ideas, a repeated assessing of original ideas against a backdrop of operational requirements. It was a practice of reining in the wilder academic ideas and of stimulating those aspects of projects that were more likely to produce tools for the operational forensic scientist. I already had many friends there and I made many others. Happily they are still my friends twenty years later, with me long into retirement. Sitting at the keyboard they are still with me in their ebullient spirits.

The Sceptical Witness

Chapter Sixteen: A Universe of Discourse

As I write the final chapter to this book there is active debate in the country on the form of government which is desirable in the United Kingdom. A change of political masters has brought new attitudes to statecraft, and the future of the second assembly, the House of Lords, is under close examination. "Reform is required" seems to be the general message of all political parties. The only point at issue appears to be its nature and extent.

Should individuals hold their positions in government simply by accident of birth? Is it acceptable that a peer of the realm enjoys his seat in the House of Lords simply because he is the descendant of the bastard offspring of a British monarch, or because a forbear gave large amounts of money to the political party that happened to be in power at the time? Or, on the other hand, is it not desirable that government should have a nucleus of tradition and stability amongst its legislators? With an upper house containing a large proportion of legislators who do not owe their positions to political favour, are we not likely to experience more mature judgement, unaffected by the winds of temporary political change? And so the argument ebbs and flows.

The essential question, stripped of all its particularities, is "who should be in charge?" The same question can be applied to all forms of management, not only the government of countries. What criteria should we apply when selecting those to be placed in authority over others? How do we distil these criteria from the total of historical experience? And what systems of government do we provide for the chosen to work in? All of which is another aspect of the search for pattern, the distinguishing of consequence from subsequence in complex experience.

My particular concern here is the selection of forensic science laboratory managers, a minor component of the global picture, one might think. The problem is that, looking back over my career and searching for pattern, I can see no real evidence that an extensive rule-guided selection procedure for laboratory managers performs any better than the application of the time honoured "Buggins' turn" method. This may be taken either as a counsel of despair or as a comforting indication of the resilience of the natural order of things against human interference, dependent upon one's personal preferences. There are, of course, compelling reasons why any individual chosen to do a job should be the best qualified to perform it. Unhappily the criteria for successful managerial appointments in many fields, including laboratory administration, remain to be fully identified. The profit motive is hardly one that can be applied here and so one has to act in the absence of that most indicative of documents, the balance sheet.

During my career I have been closely associated with two long serving laboratory managers who had faced no competition throughout their entire working lives. Having been appointed to one-man units they simply remained in post as the successive burgeoning of staff numbers carried them upwards in their progressively more influential positions. The net result of this was to produce two of the most effective laboratory managers I have ever known. If my own performance were assessed to be at the same level I would be more than satisfied.

This is not a plea for a *laissez faire* attitude towards the appointment of those in authority. It is simply an illustration that things are not so simple as they may superficially appear. A wholesome scepticism should be maintained towards those who believe they have found the template for managerial appointments procedures. The strength with which I hold this view is increased by the fact that I know other laboratory managers, appointed in the teeth of fierce competition and through the most formalised and extensive of processes, who have subsequently proved to be very much less than effective. And, of course, we must live with the modern view that management appointments in the public domain must be conditioned by a substantial element of social engineering.

In my own case my appointment carried something of the inevitable about it. With a modest research record at a time when most of my colleagues had none, and having served as deputy at the Central Research Establishment for two years followed by six years as an operational laboratory director, I believe that most thought my appointment to be inevitable, on a *faute de mieux* basis. I was rather pleased that it was. The service was increasing in size as the value of forensic science to the community became evident and there were several members of my new staff whom I would have had great difficulty competing with had we all been of the same age and experience.

My predecessor in the job had built the laboratory up to an international stature that was the object of universal admiration throughout the world of forensic science. He was a man of profound erudition, intellectual independence and he had a highly distinctive management method. He was also a most likeable person. Of course he could not enjoy so many human virtues without possessing human faults. His major flaw was that he was a very poor judge of character and he tended to accept people on their face values. But his successor arguably suffered an even worse defect because he had a double dose of scepticism towards most human motives and endeavours. So it was inevitable that the management style should change. In itself this was no bad thing. There are many different ways of killing a cat.

But at least I was determined that management would not change in one respect and that was in the relationship of the director to higher authority. My predecessor had established a happy relationship with his own boss who was located in London on one of the extensive corridors of the Civil Service. The link had been one where the distant authority had been content to leave research affairs in the hands of the man on the spot and the man on the spot much preferred it that way. But now the roles had changed. My predecessor had metamorphosed into the distant authority and I had become the man on the spot. It soon became evident that my determination to maintain managerial independence would necessitate continual battling. Not that I was averse to a battle or two but chronic strife can be somewhat distracting from the important problems.

But whatever strife existed was compensated by the joy of being able to work with such a group of mentally active people as constituted my new staff. Discussions on past, current and planned research topics took up a large part of my time and I found these meetings to be the highlights of my working days. The whole laboratory, intellectually, was one large universe of discourse. Seminars were often spiced by the leader being a newly appointed scientist fresh from his doctoral studies at university. This had the strength that the latest academic research findings were at the fingertips of the new staff member. It had the weakness that it was difficult in some cases to convince individuals that academic research findings must be adapted to operational requirements and not vice versa.

As one who throughout his life as an operational forensic scientist had been hoping for more opportunity to indulge in research it came as something of a shock to realise that most operational scientists found the prospects of being a researcher to be less than inviting. The consequence was that few operational scientists moved from their posts and the vacant research positions were taken up by academics. But the balance was not grossly distorted towards academicism. At least I had a nucleus of experienced forensic scientists to help in the business of sealing off the more inviting primrose paths.

I took the opportunity as soon as possible after my arrival to make the management structure a much leaner one. In so doing I increased my effective research strength by moving scientists from their desks back to the laboratory bench. The changes were not universally popular but they soon proved effective. It is so easy in any organisation for managerial functions to increase progressively without any related increase in productivity. I suppose it is one of the joys of a manager to cut out what he considers to be dead-wood functions and to see a leaner organisation performing even better than before. My extensive management changes were made in a climate of predicted major consequential disasters. None of these came to pass.

The mood abroad in forensic science at the time was one of great activity in research, and money was fairly easy to come by when careful plans were laid to obtain it. My aim was the normal one of the

Chapter Sixteen: A Universe of Discourse

research manager. It was to maximise the number of operationally useful findings at a minimum cost. This required that I should be something of a scientific oracle. Which projects should I encourage and which projects should I axe? Should I allow a hitherto unproductive line of research to continue after several years simply because the specialist researchers involved assured me that useful results would be finally forthcoming? Specialist researchers are always confident for the future and one can only sympathise with them if their line of investigation is axed by someone whom they feel is less than competent to make such a specialised decision.

A good example of this type of research related to a topic which was extremely interesting to me personally because it dealt with the individuality of human body fluids. It was in this field that my own modest research record existed. In a previous chapter I have described how forensic scientists seek to establish the individual nature of blood and bloodstains by identifying blood groups. These are genetically inherited, constant and lifelong characteristics. Their identification in case material is of long established value in the history of forensic science. The research topic I am about to describe, however, dealt with the problem from the standpoint of acquired characteristics. This was a very different direction of approach to the individualisation of bloodstains.

Human beings, like all living organisms, are conditioned both by inheritance and by the environment. Put succinctly, as one Victorian biologist did, they are a consequence of "Nature and Nurture". The genetic characteristics of the human body comprise the "Nature" and they do not change throughout ones life. They are the factorial instructions upon which the development of the organism largely depends. The fact that a particular organism is defined as "human" is dependent upon these factors. But many other characteristics do change and these are the consequence of "Nurture". One of these facultative properties, stimulated by the environment, is the generation in blood of protective antibodies to disease organisms. These antibodies tend to confer immunity to particular diseases and they are a specific reaction of the body to infection by a specific disease organism. Each antibody generated in this way is highly distinctive in nature and it is peculiar to a single disease. Often it persists in the bloodstream long after the infection has disappeared. Hence the property of some individuals of being immune to certain diseases. This, of course, is the basis of the practice of immunisation in which disease organisms with their infectious properties artificially suppressed are used to stimulate an immunity without generating a clinical infection.

Now the presence or absence of such antibodies in blood is of supreme clinical importance in conditioning the progress of a disease but we, as forensic scientists, were only concerned with the cataloguing aspect. Why not use such characteristics, hitherto of only clinical significance, in the field of forensic individualisation? Consider the situation where a murder victim carries in his blood antibodies which are a lasting result of him suffering from a certain tropical disease some years before. Now if during the attack a killer picks up stains of the victim's blood on his clothing the presence of such antibodies in the bloodstains could be a highly characterising feature. This is particularly so if the killing occurred in a temperate country where the disease does not exist.

A murder jury might even find such evidence more digestible than formal blood group evidence. After all if evidence is given that a murder victim worked, some years before his death, in a tropical country where he suffered an attack of yellow fever, then evidence that bloodstains on the accused's clothing contain antibodies to the virus of yellow fever might be viewed as highly significant. Taken in conjunction with the other evidence, scientific and non scientific, this could be the evidential factor which finally convinces the jury of the guilt of the accused. Even at the present time, with the evidential successes of DNA characterisation widely known amongst the public, a demonstration of previous infection might be taken as a more familiar and less esoteric finding upon which a jury would be happier to base a verdict. But at the time of which I write DNA characterisation had not advanced to the status of a dream much less to a forensic technique.

Chapter Sixteen: A Universe of Discourse

So it was with great interest that I viewed one of the external contracts which I found under way on my return to CRE. This was concerned with the identification of various viral antibodies in bloodstains. Located in a university setting the project was led by an eminent specialist who, apart from his academic achievements, was a thoroughly civilised and educated individual whose expertise was modulated by extreme kindness and courtesy. I found my conferences with him to be highly informative and enjoyable. The project was fairly advanced and it had already been found possible to demonstrate a small range of viral antibodies in bloodstains. The problem now was to demonstrate that the technique was sufficiently reliable to make it generally available to the forensic science laboratories for routine use.

For the method to be generally adopted one had to be certain that it did not give false positive results. That is to say that an antibody to a particular virus must not be identified by the technique if the antibody is not present in the bloodstain. This is a pretty obvious precondition for any forensic technique. One must not find what is not there. But there is a parallel requirement and this is the avoidance of false negative results. Here the situation is somewhat more complex. Assuming adequate technical competence what is the significance of a failure to find a particular antibody in a bloodstain?

Such a result could mean either that it was not present in the original liquid blood or that it was, but has subsequently decayed. In the clinical context this ambiguity is usually absent because storage conditions are chosen to avoid sample deterioration. But the forensic scientist does not choose the storage conditions of his samples. He has to take what he finds and do the best he can. So if a competent forensic scientist identifies a particular factor in a bloodstain then it can be stated with confidence that it is there. If he fails to identify the factor in the bloodstain it can mean either that it was not there in the original fresh sample, or that it was but has now decayed beyond the limits of detectability.

The Sceptical Witness

In the virus study I found that false negatives were fairly common when experimental bloodstains were examined but I didn't consider this as fatal to the project. One could view the results under such circumstances as a question of "factor positive" or "factor indeterminate". In other words the scientist could say either that the factor was there in the original liquid blood or that he didn't know whether it was or not. This is a conceptual matter that is illuminated by thought experiments but these I will leave to the reader. Unhappily the results produced by the external contractor also showed a number of false positives and these I considered unacceptable. In forensic science it is inadmissible to find what is not there. I made my views known to the external contractor but performance in this aspect did not improve. So I axed the contract.

The cancellation was a distressing occasion for the contractor and a very uncomfortable time for me. The trouble under such circumstances is that the factors involved are both scientific and human. In this case some bitterness was generated but I saw no point in pouring more of the taxpayer's money into a project that held no prospect of success in the foreseeable future. In addition there was the normal incomprehension of the specialist who cannot understand how it is that a non-specialist has the power, and effrontery, to axe his pet project. So it was an unhappy interlude.

It also generated an "underspend" on the contracts funding and, with yearly estimates and the lengthy assessment required before for the adoption of new contracts, it is easy to see that a regular throughput of research funds could easily be extinguished by a too robust axing of current contracts. But my working class origins were a powerful influence in my attitudes to spending. I saw no point in wasting the taxpayer's good money on unpromising projects. Perhaps I was wrong. Perhaps most government spending on research is a "waste" when judged by immediate "results". Pouring public money into chronically unproductive medical and scientific projects is a habit of mankind and it simply reflects the hope and the desire of society that the projects *should* succeed and the willingness of professionals to try to *make* them succeed. But there is an added factor to be considered by any research manager when he reviews any research topic of doubtful productivity. This is that when a promising research topic does arise there should be a viable and relevant research team readily available. If institutions and their teams founder when a research topic is axed this means fewer trained individuals ready for the productive topics when they arise. The over-energetic axing of currently unproductive research projects can leave something of an experimental wasteland. Everyone needs practice.

Then there is the difficulty of saying, and getting, what one wants. It is very difficult to define a research topic in a totally unambiguous way. Every definition of requirements is usually interpretable in a dozen different ways. Each restrictive clause in an experimental design is likewise often ambiguous. Anyone who has worked at a bench with a new assistant knows that it only requires a short time for experimental practices to drift away from those required even with the scientist and his assistant in the same room. And the more intelligent and imaginative the assistant the more the drift. Consider then the additional opportunities for ambiguity where experimental work is being carried out under contract hundreds of miles away from the centre of direction.

Those external contracts which have proved remarkably successful in producing new methods in forensic science have tended to be the ones where the project had already been carried to a very advanced stage at which point it was quite evident that it would prove of value in forensic science. The granting of external contract money has then been merely the icing on a preexisting cake, a late bet allowed on a winner when it was already well down the home straight. And so with such problems and many others I passed four happy and productive years tempered only by chronic interference from above from an intellect much too active and imaginative to be restrained by mere administrative tasks.

My service as director was interrupted by an invitation to join a small group of high ranking police officers in assessing the progress of a long running investigation into a series of murders. This took me away from the laboratory for about six months and, on my return, many changes were noticeable. These were partly due to drift but largely due to managerial interference. My relationship with my boss was at its lowest ebb and I saw little point in remaining in my job simply to repair what I viewed as other peoples' errors. So I took these changes as a signal to ask for a transfer to an operational laboratory and then, after a year or so, to retire with a consultancy appointment.

The object of my consultancy was to write a book on the scientific investigation of crime. This I did to my own satisfaction but not to that of my employers. Perhaps they were expecting a recipe book of laboratory techniques. If so they were greatly disappointed. I saw the problems in crime investigation in the light of "science" in its widest sense, not to be treated solely from the standpoint of the scene of crime and the laboratory. My theme was very much a conceptual one which dealt with attitudes, ideas and systems. Now, ten years after the book's publication and long after it went out of print I begin to see the adoption, sometimes rather clumsily, of the ideas and practices that I advocated.

Crime investigation is a high grade intellectual pursuit, a fact that is obscured by there being a large proportion of "easily solved" crimes. Many more cases of this type of crime could be solved simply by applying more resources to them. Any criminal investigation department has only a limited staff and limited time. But success in solving everyday crime can obscure failure in the unusual ones such as serial murders. One should keep this in mind when reading crime statistics. Limited as I am nowadays to getting much of my crime investigation news from the newspapers it is evident that the idea of the high grade crime investigator is catching on. It may be argued that it is a pretty obvious idea but it certainly was not so when I was a working forensic scientist. In those days although the good detectives and investigators may have gravitated towards the job there was precious little evidence of the active selection of the best qualified people.

Chapter Sixteen: A Universe of Discourse

Looking to the future it may be that many of the most interesting problems in crime investigation will disappear with the progressive adoption of modern security surveillance and identification techniques. Video surveillance of public places is very common nowadays and there is little evidence of public resentment to this. Rather the opposite. In parallel with the increasing use of surveillance methods the techniques of personal identification have advanced greatly over the past ten years. The automatic reading and sorting of fingerprints has made identifications possible which would hardly have been attempted in the old "manual" days. Modern image scanning methods, and computer processing of the resulting data, have made possible the establishment of personal identity without the transfer of any physical traces at all. Currently an individual at a cash point may establish identity by the pattern of the iris of his eye, the whole process being carried out automatically.

I see all this progress as very heartening. Our criminal court juries are receiving higher and higher grade scientific evidence in establishing the "facts" of a case with a consequential improvement in the accuracy of their verdicts. But the day when intent may be identified and measured by a "scientific" technique seem, happily, as far away as ever. One thing is certain, changes will continue to be made and not always for the best. The wisdom in Lord Falkland's dictum is yet to be generally recognised.

When it is not necessary to change it is necessary not to change.

But this is not a plea for the *status quo antes* but simply a plea for all interested parties to think deeply before change is implemented. Particularly one should beware of the presenting of sectional interests under the guise of that which is desirable for the public good. All those concerned should bring to their examination of proposed changes a sophisticated and sceptical attitude, keeping in mind that scepticism without consideration of all the evidence is simply prejudice.

The Sceptical Witness

One of the most surprising developments over the past twenty years has been the development of the view that all evidence in the criminal trial is essentially scalar. This notion has its origin in the fact that much scientific evidence can be expressed in figures. The most public indication of the use of numerical evidence is probably now that which occurs when evidence of DNA characterisation is given in court. A forensic biologist in such a case will testify that he has examined a stain of blood or other body fluid and he can find no points of difference with his findings from the examination of a comparison sample from a suspected individual. Obviously the worth of such a finding is dependent upon the frequency with which he would expect to find matching examples in the population at large. It is of little value, as incriminatory evidence, if I say that the blood from individual X matches the blood from individual Y using a particular set of factors, if that set of factors occurs in fully half the population at large. If the factor set occurred only in a much smaller proportion of the community it would be of a much higher probative value. Under such circumstances it is fully permissible, and indeed necessary, that a figure be placed on the evidence. For example I might say that the crime sample of blood from the clothing of the accused matches the blood of the defendant with regard to a particular set of DNA characteristics. I might then go on to say that this particular set of characteristics occurs in only one in a million individuals in the population at large. Then I might want to introduce the concept of probability by saying that this means that if I picked any individual at random from the population, the chance of me happening across a matching blood would be one in a million.

At this stage some alert member of the jury may say to himself that one should also take into account the probability that an innocent person would have bloodstains on his clothing anyway. This is perfectly valid but, conceptually and numerically, we are entering a domain of much greater complexity here. Bloodstains of any shape? Bloodstains of any size? Bloodstains in any position? Each of these factors may be of evidential value but putting figures to such variable circumstances is far more difficult than counting or calculating the number of people with such and such a blood group combination.

Now go one step further and consider ascribing probabilities to the various occurrences which are the subject of evidence, not merely expert evidence, in the criminal trial. Can we do this and if so can we combine these probabilities in such a way that a jury might find it useful in coming to their verdict? Who should ascribe the probabilities to the commonplace (in general) but unique (in particular) events which make up the detail of evidence given in the criminal trial? All this may seem laughably ingenuous but dedicated system-mongers have a habit of succeeding when initially their efforts seemed to constitute no more than amusing academicism. No-one can predict the direction that law and procedure will develop in the future with any degree of certainty. There are too many variables. Those of us who have lived a long time have seen changes in the law which, had they been proposed thirty years ago, would have been immediately dismissed as bizarre imaginings. Now they are fact.

There is a sinister aspect to this too. When it is pointed out that most members of society are innumerate to the degree that they would find it difficult to use such ideas and make such calculations it is smoothly proposed that they needn't do so, the experts would do it for them. What sort of experts? The answer in general is the experts who are experts at coming to decisions for other people. They are the priesthoods which abound in all societies.

I must declare an interest here. I passionately believe in the jury system of criminal trial. I believe in a system where an accused is judged, on matters of fact, by his peers and that, for me under English law, is the juryman or the unpaid magistrate. I cannot understand why lawyers are taken, *qua lawyers*, to be better judges of fact than non-lawyers. I have seen no evidence that they are in almost fifty years as a servant of the court and that is what I, long into retirement, still consider myself to be. I believe the jury system of criminal trial is very imperfect but I equally believe that no-one has come up with a better one.

The Sceptical Witness

I doubt if juries stand in imminent danger of being supplanted by "experts" but the suggestion that they should be is a hardy perennial. A quarter century ago I attended a London meeting of the Forensic Science Society. The speaker was a High Court judge, a most able and impressive lecturer, and he spoke for an interesting hour on the subject of criminal trial procedure. The discussion which followed drifted into the realms of the desirability or otherwise of expert decision makers to displace the jury. At the time of the meeting I was the editor of the Society's journal and, as such, I had few official duties to perform. So, comfortably established on the back row of the audience and with the discussion taking familiar paths I rested my chin on my chest and went to sleep. I had heard all the arguments before.

A feeling of unease crept into my sleeping mind and I stirred and woke up to find the entire audience swivelled in their chairs and with eyes firmly fixed upon me. In the background was the insistent voice of the chairman saying that the audience would now have the benefit of the views of the editor on the question which had been raised. There was no way of getting out of it despite the fact I had no idea of what the question was. I dragged myself to my feet, hastily brushing the clouds of sleep from my mind and desperately tried to remember the last words I had heard before I fell into the arms of Morpheus.

Then, fortified by the knowledge that at least half of the audience would think they had missed the point if I started to speak of some totally irrelevant matter, I launched into a few background remarks about the criminal trial and then, with the fervour of an old style evangelist, I made the point that, science and law apart, we must never abolish the jury system and substitute it by a panel of experts, if for no other reason than the fact that it would be interpreted by the public as "them" standing in judgement of "us".

It wasn't science, and many members of the audience looked at me with total disbelief that one of their fellows should introduce such a populist factor into a learned discussion. I began to anticipate trouble. But then I noticed I had an important ally. The High Court judge, our main speaker, was nodding in vigorous agreement with me and I knew I was home and dry. I made a few more remarks and sat down. Then the judge rose to his feet, agreed with everything I had said and proceeded to hammer the final scholarly nails into the populist coffin which I had just produced for the anti-jury faction. He did it with the proficiency conferred by a lifetime of expert advocacy and, bathing in reflected glory and safe in the knowledge that I had left the matter in the safest of hands, I drifted back to sleep.

I came into forensic science by accident as this book shows and I started my career full of doubt and misgiving about its value to society when compared to other parts of applied science. I no longer harbour doubts. It has been a privilege to belong to a profession which has developed beyond what anyone could have imagined fifty years ago. I see the function of forensic science in crime investigation and the criminal trial quite clearly. It is that of the cartographer. It is the provision of the physical scale, the bench-marks, the way-points and the boundary-posts which occur on the rough and irregular terrain which has to be traversed by the investigating officer and the court. Similarly I see the function of the criminal lawyer as that of production engineer in the trial process.

We must always keep in mind the asymmetry of the criminal trial process. It is not a question of deciding between "guilty" and "innocent" but between "guilty" and "don't know" . The "not guilty" verdict is in essence the default verdict, a declaration that the prosecution has failed in its case. It is not a declaration of innocence except inasmuch as the presumption of innocence is not invalidated. But presumption is not proof as newspaper readers should keep in mind each time the headlines announce a miscarriage of justice.

I was amused when a colleague recounted to me the treatment he had received at the hands of defence counsel when giving evidence on blood alcohol in a case of "driving under the influence".

The Sceptical Witness

Counsel "All knowledge is provisional, is it not?"

Witness "In a sense it is, but I am sure of my facts in this case"

Counsel "Come now, you scientists used to believe the sun went round the earth!"

The good natured banter that followed, including the judge's ruling on "hearsay evidence", must not be allowed to obscure the fact that counsel was right. All knowledge is provisional but we live in a real world where provisional knowledge must be used as a definitive basis for action. We must operate on a basis of what appears to be reasonable at the time. Yet we must always keep in mind the limitations of human decision making and must recognise that we, ourselves, may be the victim of these limitations one day. If so, and we fail to have the matter righted, I believe that it is a price we have to pay in a democratic society for the built-in imperfections of our decision making systems. It's not much comfort to the wrongly convicted, I admit, but perhaps it is better than nothing. It is at least better than being convicted by denunciation, fatwa or witchcraft. But we must always retain a critical attitude to our scientific beliefs and procedures and not consider them carved into tablets of stone..

Just one last example of an incident which proved formative in my scientific life and which, I believe unfortunately, places me in a minority amongst my scientific colleagues. Some twenty years ago I was at a loose end one evening and I noticed an advertisement in the local paper. This announced a lecture on "creationism", the anti Darwinist notion that life as we see it today is a consequence of a single act of genesis rather than the culmination of a (still evolving) series of events. I went to the lecture with the intention of being amused rather than instructed. What other attitude could an orthodox scientist hold other than that Darwin adequately explained the outline of our origins and that modern genetics explained the mechanism?

Chapter Sixteen: A Universe of Discourse

No, you are wrong. There follows no account of conversion or revelation. I came away with my beliefs unshaken but with a new respect for the other side's point of view. The orthodox biologist's view of creationists (at least the ones who organised this meeting) as bubbling loonies was quite wrong. The lecturer was a local surgeon, a most excellent and logical speaker, and I was fascinated by his theme. Before leaving the lecture hall I bought a couple of books which became the basis of a small creationist library in my study. Much of this literature is very well written, closely reasoned and very enjoyable to read. But I believe the creationists are wrong so why do I continue to read the stuff? Simply because they provide plausible, and some telling, arguments as to why I should not believe what I believe. They make it so that my scientific beliefs are leaner and fitter to survive than before I listened to the creationists. As far as I am concerned they are part of the harsh and demanding environment which my beliefs have to battle in order to survive. Isn't that what science is all about?

But it is a dangerous attitude for a scientist to hold. Once a theory has become well established then the opposing points of view tend to be forgotten. After all, why reconsider rubbish? Life is short. One cannot consider all problems from first principles or from every point of view. All that such an "open to argument" attitude is likely to attract from ones colleagues is a distaste that a professional scientist should waste his time considering unscientific rubbish. So be it. But, in my study, the creationist books are shelved next to the ones on crop circles and astrology. That is to say they are on the shelf above those written by Velikovsky.

Always remember one's theory may be a cuckoo. It may sit comfortably in the orthodox nest having disposed of all other fledgling theories over the edge, and being fed and nurtured by guardians who do not recognise its true nature. This applies to both the theories of scientists and to the hunches of crime investigators, although to differing degrees. The cuckoo analogy may be stretched even further. In England we have a national pastime for recording the arrival of the first immigrant cuckoo of the year. Over the years the advent of its distinctive call is recorded on thousands of occasions in the newspapers, including in that most august of journals, the Times of London. Unfortunately such records are rendered unreliable by an equally national pastime, that of hoaxing.

I have personally known a very accomplished hoaxer who could produce a cuckoo call of such quality as to take in most, if not all, of those who heard it. Over each succeeding year he saw the announcement of the progressively earlier arrivals of his "cuckoo" in the pages of the local press. Each announcement was mediated by observers who had heard the "cuckoo call" and taken it as a genuine one. And there is nothing like a desire to be the first to announce a discovery or observation. So our observations may be imaginary cuckoos and our theories may be real ones. It is a confusing world.

As readers of this book will have noticed I have problems with the concept of "time". Life is a single picture for me, resplendent in its many dimensions all painted on to a single canvas. Time is but one of these dimensions. Almost forty years after the war I went to a city in north Germany to take part in a forensic science symposium. I had a colleague with me, a much younger man. As our aircraft approached the destination airport my mind drifted to a previous, and very different, visit I had made to this city. In an instant the intervening years dissolved away as if they had never been.

The shell bursts drifted nearer to the aircraft and I experienced once again the cold, gut wrenching terror. I felt as if I was going to vomit and the sweat ran freely down my neck and dribbled down my chest. I clenched my fists hard and felt myself begin to shake. In the distance there was there was a small and insistent voice. It came closer.

"Pilot to navigator, pilot to navigator, answer please".

I tried to answer through my clenched teeth and through the engine noise and the muffled explosions, but the words refused to come. The voice returned.

Chapter Sixteen: A Universe of Discourse

"Are you all right, Stuart?"

I shook myself back into the present and my colleague's concerned face swam into my field of vision. Gradually I recovered composure.

"I'm fine thank you. A touch of airsickness".

With a look of concern still on his face my companion slowly relaxed back into his seat but kept his eyes on me as he tried to make conversation.

"Have you been here before?" he said.

"Yes, just once" I said dully, with the sickness remaining deep in my stomach.

"Was that a scientific meeting?" he said.

I replied that it wasn't.

Then what were you doing here?" he asked innocently.

"I was dropping bombs" I replied.

And the terror began to return.

The Sceptical Witness